HOW PHARMACISTS LEAD

Answers from Women Who Are Leading, Succeeding, and Impacting Pharmacy

Hillary Blackburn
PharmD, MBA

Praise for *How Pharmacists Lead*

"I was first introduced to Hillary's work a few years ago through her podcast Talk to Your Pharmacist and met her personally for a Mastermind weekend in Nashville. She has always been passionate about female leadership and empowering women in pharmacy. I was so inspired by the stories of the women featured in the book, and I look forward to our bright future as leaders!" - Blair Thielemier, PharmD, CEO of Pharmapreneur Academy

"Hillary's book explores the possibilities allowing women pharmacists to dream big, becoming leaders, entrepreneurs, social networkers, clinicians and the best health care providers they can be. These women do not sit by waiting for opportunities to come; they create and plan their successes in a variety of career paths." - Kelby Kuhn, PharmD, Medical Science Liaison, AstraZeneca Pharmaceuticals

"Dr. Blackburn's timely book on women in pharmacy leadership fills a great need in our profession. I have been truly blessed in my career to be influenced by many wonderful leaders and many of them happen to be women. Dr. Blackburn is one of those rising leaders." - David Gregory, Dean, Belmont University College of Pharmacy

"This book offers inspiring and compelling examples of pharmacists embracing change and successfully pivoting through their career. Additionally, it offers tangible and actionable ways to develop your own leadership journey." - Molly Ekstrand, BPharm, BCACP, AE-C, North Star Medication Optimization LLC

"*How Pharmacists Lead* takes a critical look at the role of women in pharmacy, including the challenges that sometimes lay in their path. As a female CEO of an online pharmacy, I heartily recommend Blackburn's book to women pursuing pharmacy as both an honest and inspiring portrayal of how we're poised to lead healthcare forward." - Jessica Nouhavandi, PharmD, CEO of Honeybee Health

Dedication

Thankful to all the women who have blazed the trails before us: those serving as role models, our biggest cheerleaders, and those who challenge us to keep breaking boundaries. As we strive to lead in the profession, let's help nurture the next female leaders. By mentoring the many others coming after us, we can help other women advance in their careers.

And to my mother, a former English teacher (whom I even had as a teacher for three years in high school) who served as an editor to get this book ready for publication, as well as role modeled and encouraged me to be the leader that I am today. As well as my mother-in-law, a true trailblazer as the first female Senator from Tennessee, and sister-in-law who are both accomplished females and role models.

Contents

Table of Contents

Introduction

By definition, a leader best leads by example; and today's world needs role models, or examples, to inspire and motivate us. I've been blessed to be working with and surrounded by strong female leaders. While there were several female pharmacy leaders who served as mentors for me as I was progressing through pharmacy school, two who made a particular impact on me were Dr. Deborah Minor and Dr. Sharon Dickey. It wasn't a surprise that I continued to select them as preceptors during pharmacy school so that I could soak up clinical knowledge and life skills from them during my 3rd and 4th year clinical rotations and even through an additional year as a PGY-1 Pharmacy Practice resident since they oversaw the University of Mississippi Medical Center's pharmacy residency program. These women have a depth of clinical experience and a passion for mentoring others, as well as a desire for serving in their communities. They also instilled a strong work ethic in their students, as I vividly remember a conversation with Dr. Minor during an early rotation saying, "If you don't have something to do, there's been a misunderstanding." They wanted us to stay busy – learning!

This book aims to inspire readers, particularly young aspiring females, along their own leadership journey by acknowledging challenges along the path and highlighting examples of women in pharmacy who are leading, succeeding, and making an impact.

CHAPTER 1

THE NEED FOR FEMALE LEADERS

The shift toward more women in the workforce began post World War II. Women, like Rosie the Riveter, had jumped in to help outside the home in factories while the men were off at war or they were serving as nurses on the frontlines to tend to those injured. Over the next few decades, families slowly started to shift from single income families to dual income families. By 2018, the United States Bureau of Labor Statistics reported that 57.1% of all women were in the labor force, compared to 69.1% of all men.

For a number of years, women have chosen careers in healthcare, historically in nursing. Now, women are also choosing other health professions such as pharmacy and medicine where the flexibility and ability to make good incomes has been a draw. The healthcare professions have traditionally been dominated by males, but this trend has changed in the pharmacy profession where a gradual shift has occurred. Females now make up the majority of graduates in the health professions, including pharmacy. In 2017-2018, women made up over 60% of the pharmacy degrees conferred in according to the

American Association of Colleges of Pharmacy's Vital Statistics.

However, the state of female leadership in the country, especially in the healthcare industry remains dismal. Women make up 80% of the healthcare workforce, but only 3% hold the title of CEO, 6% are department chairs, 9% are division chiefs and 3% are chief medical officers (Rotenstein, 2018). In the business community, the percentage of women on company boards differs from country to country and in the US, this number is roughly about 17% (Catalyst, 2020). Ultimately, the number of women at top positions within companies has been pretty stagnant.

Women are not often top of mind when one thinks of leadership. If you search for books on leadership, you'll find that most of the authors are males. And as of 2020, there has still never been a female U.S. President and there are far fewer women than men representing us in leadership roles in Congress.

Why the Female Leadership Gap?

While women make the majority of healthcare decisions for their households, they are not at the top making decisions for companies (Luce, 2015). There could be many factors contributing to this including the perception of the incongruity of women with leadership roles (Paustian-Underdahl, 2014). In other words, people still in the 1950s mindset of a single earner family dynamic where women stay at home while men go to work. Women have long faced the duality of balancing work and home life. Although women do work outside the home, many today still prefer to work from the home, especially if their financial situations allow.

Other factors contributing to the lack of female leaders could include: many women choosing not to seek the top jobs or failing to obtain needed qualifications or scaling back their career demands to balance family since these duties often fall on the woman. Many factors may be self-imposed, yet women's advancement may not be fostered or facilitated at organizations due to a number of reasons including gender prejudice or the fact that they permit a culture that is inhospitable to women (Bilimoria, 2012). Maybe another cause for this gap is the fact that women are undervalued as leaders?

According to Bilimoria, there are organizational (higher standards for women), interpersonal (lack of mentors or stereotypes) and personal barriers (home life responsibilities). First-generation biases are overt and deliberate, whereas second-generation biases are more inadvertent and unconscious. Second generation biases include gendered career paths. In other words, men go into certain roles and women go into others, the lack of role models for women, and women's lack of access to networks (Ely, 2013). There are often stereotypes that exist for certain roles, particularly in healthcare such as the hasty and baseless assumption that women are generally nurses and men are generally physicians.

The leadership consultant firm Zenger Folkman pulled several studies to examine women in leadership and found out that women outperformed their male counterparts in overall effectiveness, 54% to 51% (Sherwin, 2014). Sherwin points out that although men's effectiveness maintains consistency over time, as women mature their effectiveness increases due to their continued commitment to asking for feedback. Women continue to practice self-development upon receiving this feedback. The Sherwin article also lists several competencies as determined in a study by Zenger Folkman in which women excel including but not limited to:

- Motivating others
- Fostering communication
- Producing high-quality work
- Listening to others
- Building relationships

Leadership Styles: Trait, Situational, Servant, and Transformational

While completing my MBA degree, I revisited what it means to be a leader and to lead. One of our first assignments dealt with leadership: identifying the qualities of a leader and what qualities lead to the best leadership styles. I began this assignment by considering my own innate leadership qualities and reflecting on the leadership positions, such as head cheerleader and soccer team captain, to which a younger me was selected. I thought about ***why*** my peers had selected me to these positions and what I could learn from that knowledge. Undoubtedly, my aptitude for cheerleading and organized sports such as soccer, as well as my inner drive and organizational skills certainly contributed to my selection as a "leader." I also note that the aforementioned typical leadership characteristics (aptitude, organization, and inner drive) fit the "trait leader" category as described by Khan (2016).

While further studying leadership during my MBA, I found that leadership styles need to be dynamic. But it is important to find and follow good role models and then model leadership yourself. Initially, you need to build a foundation based on "trait" leadership, which for pharmacy students begins with a firm educational background. Never stop learning and be an example to others by staying on top of scientific breakthroughs, new drug approvals, etc.

Next, leaders must remember that it is important to serve. Another leadership style is "servant" leadership (Khan, 2016). It is important to serve, and by serving or volunteering, you may find that new opportunities come your way. As pharmacists, we are seen as leaders in the community and should be committed to being involved and serving others around us in and out of the pharmacy. Volunteering provides a great way to practice servant leadership. And sometimes, gaining skills and developing relationships as a volunteer might even lead to opportunities. For instance, I served as a volunteer while working another full-time job but that opened the door when the first and only pharmacist position became available at Dispensary of Hope, a nonprofit medication distribution company headquartered in Nashville, Tennessee.

Upon joining the Dispensary of Hope (DoH), I put my innate trait leader characteristics into practice, worked hard, proved my value, and assumed more administrative responsibilities within my organization. This led to my official inclusion into the leadership team merely a year after my hire date. The DoH leadership team valued my expertise and leadership qualities as an added asset. My quick elevation to the leadership team confirms that experience (as opposed to tenure) may move you up more quickly in our knowledge era as Peter Drucker (2002) suggests.

As I have matured, my leadership has evolved into a more situational leadership style (Khan, 2016). This means that I lead mostly with my individualization strength and often adapt my style to the situation. For instance, when I am precepting or leading my rotational student pharmacists, my leadership style is more task focused. Once they complete a project successfully, then I move them onto the next as they prove mastery of more and more challenging tasks. While in a different case, such as when I'm running a meeting with my pharmacist peers who serve on a volunteer advisory council for DoH, I lean towards a participative style. Overall, depending on the people with whom I'm interacting and their knowledge base, I adapt my style to fit my environment moving between task and relational (Khan, 2016). During my organization's Leadership Team meetings where I have been the newest (and youngest) member, I listen more and learn from others but speak up confidently during discussions involving my areas of expertise or concern.

Learning how to lead in the business setting has become increasingly fascinating to me as I have moved from a primarily clinical role to an administrative one. To increase my own self-awareness, I have embraced tools including personality tests such as the CliftonStrengthsFinder, Enneagram, and DISC profiles.

Truity offers and describes the Enneagram as a personality test consisting of nine types (perfectionist, giver, achiever, individualist, investigator, skeptic, enthusiast, challenger, peacemaker) that shape a person's worldview. The DiSCProfile describes the DiSC assessment as a "non-judgmental tool used for discussion of people's behavioral differences." Finally, Gallup's CliftonStrengths assessment consists of 34 unique strengths that are ranked upon taking the test to provide better insight into being your best self and "playing to [those] strengths at work and everywhere else." These tests should reinforce what you already know about yourself. For example, my Enneagram test identified three personalities that I rotate between: enthusiast, reformer, and achiever.

My passion for connecting with and sharing the stories of inspiring leaders led me to found, host, and produce a pharmacy focused podcast in August 2017 called *Talk to Your Pharmacist.* A goal of the podcast is to create awareness of issues relating to the profession and transform the mindset of pharmacists to engage in a broader vision of healthcare globally vs. the microcosm of their day job. This goal of professional transformation is more reflective of transformational leadership, a more popular leadership style in today's workplace.

What is 21st Century Leadership?

The 21st Century fully embraces the transformational leadership style. Transformational leadership builds others up which positively fosters improved performance and culture and contributes to an organization's desired outcomes (Brown 2009). This leadership style is particularly effective when managing significant change and growth that is often experienced during the 21st century. Ideally, this transformational approach works perfectly in healthcare settings which are particularly focused on achieving better outcomes as observed by Cummings, et al (2010). A blog post from Women Leadership and Twenty-First Century Challenges highlights that women demonstrate more transformational leadership than their male counterparts. To embrace this leadership style, women should lean into their skills of empowering people and mobilizing resources towards a greater purpose.

Diverse senior leadership has benefits, particularly for 21st Century organizations. For example, adding women to boards allows for more perspective, eliminating the homogeneous point of view that often arises from an all-male board. Women tend to approach decisions differently. Companies with more women financially outperform others and have higher social corporate responsibility standards.

Now, we know that there's a gap, there's the need for us to go further by highlighting women who have already paved the way and are leaders. Luckily, in pharmacy, there have been plenty of women trailblazers before us.

CHAPTER 2

WOMEN IN PHARMACY ROLE MODELS

There is a need for strong women role models, particularly those who have come before us in our respective fields. As I think back upon the "historical trailblazers" who influenced a younger me, I can see why I ultimately chose a career in healthcare.

For a third-grade book report on a biography of someone that I admire, I chose Clara Barton. Not only was Clara Barton a nurse in the Civil War and founder of the Red Cross, but she was a role model for me. Florence Nightingale is yet another well-known nurse who actually received a pin from the Red Cross in recognition of her service as a trainer of nurses during the Crimean War. Another female trailblazer in the field of science was Marie Curie, the first woman to be awarded a Nobel Prize for physics in 1903 then again for chemistry in 1911. Her discovery of radium and polonium led to breakthroughs in the field of medicine with the introduction of X-rays.

It is sometimes hard to think of a female pharmacist or physician who has made such an impact or one as prominent in history books as these trailblazers. This book highlights the careers of several female pharmacy leaders who have made the Top Women in Pharmacy list pulled from former guests on the Talk to Your Pharmacist podcast. Podcast guests include both men and women leaders, but this book focuses on some of our women guests. These are women in pharmacy leadership roles across the country that meet the following criteria:

- Have a pharmacy degree
- Work in a pharmacy setting including community pharmacy, hospital pharmacy, health insurer organization, health care research organization, physician organization, home health organization, government health agency, health care vendor, supplier organization, association, academia, or own their own pharmacy related business;
- Serve in a leadership role;
- Demonstrate that they have helped their organization "exceed" its financial, clinical, and strategic goals;
- Promote gender equity in the C-suite; and
- Act as a mentor to the next generation of leaders.

Many of the following women have had unique career paths which highlight some of the changes in the profession from a focus on community and hospital pharmacy roles to others such as consultants, authors, professors, even entrepreneurs! It is exciting to see more women as entrepreneurs because there are many benefits for female-owned businesses. In general, there is much opportunity for disruption in healthcare and a great need for more innovation from pharmacists. Sharing these examples of female leaders can help to change perceived mindsets that only males are CEOs or hold senior level positions in organizations or start run their own businesses.

The following details some of the interviews with female pharmacists featured on the podcast. ***Note:** *the below bios and stories are from podcast interviews between fall 2017 - spring 2020. Careers and specific details may have changed since the writing of this book.*

Personal Brands & Business Owners

Founder of BT PharmacyConsulting / Pharmapreneur Academy - Blair Thielemier, PharmD

www.PharmapreneurAcademy.com

Blair Thielemier, PharmD, is an independent consultant pharmacist, pharmacy business coach, virtual conference producer, and author. As a business coach, she's created a step-by-step framework for *building and "selling"* pharmacist-led clinical services called "The Pharmapreneur's Business Blueprint" and founded the Pharmapreneur Academy, an online membership community to guide pharmacist-entrepreneurs on how to build advanced clinical services. Blair is the author of How to Build a Pharmacy Consulting Business and facilitates in-person Business Mastermind Retreats and Virtual Summits for pharmapreneurs (pharmacist entrepreneurs) across the country.

Blair is a 2011 graduate of the University of Arkansas Medical Sciences Pharmacy School. She worked as a clinical hospital pharmacist until 2014 when the hospital cut her hours from full-time to PRN, which also cut her benefits. Blair was pregnant with her first child and wasn't ready to search for new full-time employment. Instead, she reached out to her local network of pharmacy friends who were pharmacy owners and needed help with relief work. These pharmacy owners also needed help managing patients eligible for medication therapy management (MTM) since they were unfamiliar with the program and not providing it, which was impacting their pharmacy's star ratings. Blair trained herself on MTM and fell in love with that clinical service so much so that she decided to build her own MTM consulting business.

As she began to build her business, Blair sought her own business coaching to help set up an LLC and build her LinkedIn presence. As she wrote posts about MTM on her blog and LinkedIn, people started reaching out to her asking, 'What is MTM consulting? … 'How do I do that? How do I translate that into my local community [to] help these independent community pharmacists, that don't have anyone to help them with the MTM program.'

In September 2015, Blair started individually coaching pharmacists on how to build these consulting relationships with their local pharmacies. Eventually, she developed a coaching program as an online course, Pharmapreneur Academy. Her consulting business has grown to include pharmacogenomic testing and working in physicians' offices. Most recently, she launched the Elevate Pharmacy virtual summit as a joint venture with the NCPA Innovation Center. Blair says, "It's been a crazy ride the last four years, but it's been the most exciting time of [my] career." Blair lives in Arkansas with her husband and three children.

To learn more from Blair and others, listen to her episode on the Talk to Your Pharmacist podcast or visit www.hillaryblackburn.com

Founder of RxAshlee - Ashlee Klevens Hayes, PharmD, MHA

https://www.rxashlee.com/

Ashlee Klevens Hayes, PharmD, MHA, is an experienced leader in hospital operations and a pharmacist career coach. She grew up in southern California and received her pharmacy degree from the University of Southern California. Then her husband's career took them to Kentucky, where she was fortunate to become the first to complete the PGY1/PGY2 pharmacy administration program at the University of Kentucky. When she finished the program, she had the opportunity to stay on as the Associate Director of Central Operations where she primarily oversaw sterile products and perioperative products services. While she served as the project manager for the implementation of new automation and technology to the pharmacy, she developed a relationship with that software company.

Ashlee left hospital practice and pursued a unique opportunity to work directly for the software company called MedKeeper as an internal consultant for product development. Then, Ashlee left to start her own venture spending about 50 percent of her time as a pharmacy operations consultant for venture capitalist or healthcare technology and software development companies and the other 50 percent providing career coaching for pharmacists. She used the transferrable skills that she has picked up throughout her career path to now fulfill her passion for coaching others. As an exceptional coach, Ashlee not only coaches just pharmacists, but since she is a pharmacist, she identifies with them as well.

To learn more from Ashlee and others, listen to her episode on the Talk to Your Pharmacist podcast or visit www.hillaryblackburn.com

Founder of The Pharmacists Guide - Joanna Lewis, PharmD, MBA

https://www.thepharmacistsguide.com/

Joanna Lewis, PharmD, MBA, is the 340B Program compliance coordinator at Baptist Health in Jacksonville, Florida and creator of the Pharmacists Guide blog. Joanna is a graduate of Medical University of South Carolina School of Pharmacy and the Citadel's MBA program. She's worked in a variety of practice settings and began the Pharmacists Guide blog as a way to connect with other pharmacists and students.

Because of her husband's residency training, she moved several times and had the opportunity to experience different jobs and develop her interests. Spending the five years in North Carolina's Research Triangle Park provided her both inspiration and opportunity as she had the chance to work with some amazing leaders and to incorporate her MBA into her practice. During this time, she had to juggle the responsibilities of parenthood with other work and life responsibilities. The stress and burnout that ensued led Joanna on a path to learning about self-care, protecting her mental health and ultimately creating The Pharmacists Guide.

In her roles as a clinical pharmacist, she worked closely with clinicians. While Joanna found that everyone enjoyed their work, she noted so much negativity everywhere, either pointed at administration or against different healthcare providers. When she moved to administration, she saw a different side of these roles. The administration team was a positive group of people who were working through building better processes, reimbursement challenges and changing technology. But so often, there was a disconnect between administration and the clinicians, leading to employees feeling underappreciated, uncertain, and overwhelmed with role ambiguity - all factors that contribute to negativity and burnout!

Joanna started The Pharmacists Guide after she left Duke (her husband took a job in Florida!). When she worked at Duke, she did a lot of process improvement and benchmarking with other organizations. That experience coupled with the passion to spread inspiration and knowledge about combating burnout led to her popular blog and eventually her other social media accounts where she daily connects with students, practitioners and other healthcare professionals both locally and internationally.

She uses her platform to teach others what factors contribute to burnout, how to build good wellness regimens and how to curate a career that you love. Mentoring students was always one of Joanna's favorite things to do at all of her jobs. So, she created a section for students: what do pharmacists do, why you should go to pharmacy school, how to get a residency interview, how to use your MBA, etc. Through the positive effects of her passion project, she's also built a leadership role in her current position and is blazing a trail in pharmacy.

She's written two e-books and currently is focused on teaching health professionals the physical, mental and emotional wellness strategies that they can incorporate into their daily lives and thus elevate their practice.

To learn more from Joanna and others, listen to her episode on the Talk to Your Pharmacist podcast or visit www.hillaryblackburn.com

Creator of StockRose Creative, LLC - Megan N. Freeland, PharmD

https://www.stockrosecreative.com

Megan N. Freeland is creator of StockRose Creative, LLC. She is originally from Columbia, South Carolina and has lived in Atlanta, Georgia, for the past decade. Previously, she worked as a public health pharmacist, specifically supporting the Centers for Disease Control and Prevention as a contractor. Megan served in several different roles while at the CDC, including medication safety, emergency preparedness, regulatory affairs, and health communications. But she stepped back from that position in 2018 when she decided to run her writing business full-time.

StockRose Creative is a healthcare copywriting and content marketing company specializing in website copy and content marketing. She offers this service as a Quarterly Content Subscription that includes 90-day content strategies for her clients, then implements those strategies by creating the content. Through StockRose, she works with a variety of health companies but specializes in digital health organizations and private health practices, including independent pharmacies and medical clinics.

In addition to StockRose, Megan is the founder of the multi-channel platform for multipassionate millennials who want to build creative, profitable lives they absolutely love. The platform includes the LaziMILLENNIAL website, The LaziMILLENNIAL

Lounge podcast, and the Multipassionate Meg YouTube channel. On the podcast, she shares stories of millennials who are in the process of building their lives through entrepreneurship, side hustles, and traditional employment. On her YouTube channel, she shares business and content strategy tips to help fellow multipassionates create and grow profitable businesses. Megan balances her business and LaziMILLENNIAL platform with being a wife and mother of two.

Hear more from Megan by listening to her episode on the Talk to Your Pharmacist podcast or visiting www.hillaryblackburn.com

Founder of Clarify, Simplify, Align - Jessica Louie, PharmD, APh, BCCP

https://drjessicalouie.com/

Jessica Louie, PharmD, APh, BCCP, is a critical care pharmacist and the CEO of Clarify, Simplify, Align. Through her business Clarify, Simpliy, & Align, Jessica coaches burned out women in healthcare create work-life harmony through simplifying and decluttering their homes, schedules and mental overload. Pursuing this life simplification also helps her clients to achieve career success, financial freedom & simple living for their family in healthcare. Jessica is a Master-level Certified KonMari Consultant and Coach, and she combines her KonMari decluttering techniques with her unique Clarify, Simplify Align method to gain clarity of purpose and align work INTO your life (and not the other way around!). Jessica hosts The Burnout Doctor Podcast weekly helping listeners with burnout, well-being, decluttering and simplifying.

After experiencing burnout herself in 2014/2015, she credits decluttering and simplifying her life as saving her from this unfulfilling time in the profession. Jessica advocates for resetting burnout (not curing it) as the method to curating a life that YOU love and creating your own definition for success in life. Simple steps that you can control in less than 10 minutes are her techniques…not waiting for organizations or corporate changes to occur. Through her process, Jessica and her partner have paid off over $300,000 in student loan debt (in less than 7 years), grown her coaching business while advancing in her academia career, and simplified to reset the shopaholic coping mechanism and mentally overloaded to-do lists that didn't serve anyone. Jessica loves helping others curate their own unique lives for simple living in healthcare families. Her coaching leads to Joy at Work and Joy at Home, and her clients range from new graduates to dual-income couples working in healthcare who have children. Simplifying to spark joy in families working in healthcare benefits everyone from parents to children to loved ones to team members and of course our patients.

Jessica is an Associate Professor in Pharmacy Practice at West Coast University (WCU) School of Pharmacy in Los Angeles, CA, and a Board-Certified Critical Care Pharmacist. Dr. Louie earned her PharmD from the University of Southern California in 2013 and completed her PGY1 in pharmacy practice and PGY2 in critical care at the University of Utah Health in Salt Lake City, UT. Additionally, she was awarded WCU Professor of the Year in 2019.

One of the main reasons Jessica went into pharmacy is the versatility and broad range of work environments pharmacists can pursue. She advocates for sharing one voice in our profession (similar to the American Medical Association) and educating the public on how pharmacists can work at the highest level of their training. Jessica sees the largest area of opportunity in ambulatory care and transitions of care, including post-ICU syndrome as patients transition out of the ICU and into a new quality of life recovering for 3-12 months after a critical illness. Jessica looks forward to pharmacists billing directly for our services just as any other healthcare professional does (i.e. speech therapist, physical therapist, dentist, etc.).

Hear more from Jessica by listening to her episode on the Talk to Your Pharmacist podcast or visit www.hillaryblackburn.com

Founder of Pharmacist Moms Group (PhMG™)- Suzanne Soliman, PharmD, BCMAS

https://www.pharmacistmomsgroup.com/

Suzanne (Suzy) Soliman, PharmD, BCMAS, is the Chief Academic Officer for the Accreditation Council for Medical Affairs (ACMA) and founder of the Pharmacist Moms Group, which includes over 35,000 members.

Suzy was born and raised in Chicago and is a graduate of the University of Illinois at Chicago College of Pharmacy (UIC). She went on to pursue additional training with an emphasis on education with a primary care residency and teaching fellowship. Suzy has worked as a Medical Science Liaison (MSL) and MSL Education/Assessment Manager for Abbott, as an Assistant/Associate Dean in academia, and owned an independent pharmacy before taking on the role at ACMA.

Suzy began her passion for education during pharmacy school when she did a rotation with one of the faculty members. She enjoyed that aspect of teaching and learning. When she did her residency, she selected one with an emphasis on education and also did a teaching fellowship because she knew that she wanted more training. Suzy shares that "because in pharmacy school, we're really prepared to become a pharmacist, but we didn't have the training on writing test questions and a lot of the educational background and components that you need to succeed as an educator." So, she looked to do a residency with a focus on education, which was really important to her. Throughout her career, she was a clinical pharmacist and a faculty member. When she became an MSL, Suzy actually developed a new role as the MSL trainer where she developed training programs and an assessment examination for all MSLs to ensure that everyone (PharmDs, MDs and PhDs) were on the same level. Suzy then went back into academia as an assistant dean to work on assessment and accreditation. She loved publications, research and academic research.

As a resident, Suzy conducted a study on academic dishonesty in pharmacy school which was published. Suzy is a recipient of the Rufus A. Lyman Award which is awarded for best manuscript published in the American Journal of Pharmaceutical Education (AJPE).

Although she loved her job at UIC as an assistant dean, when she relocated to the East Coast, Suzy wanted to find a role where she could still use her medical knowledge as a pharmacist while helping to develop programs. She found that in a role as the Chief Academic Officer with the ACMA where she works with medical affairs professionals and MSLs on training and certification. Suzy coupled her background in education and pharmacy education with her experience in pharmaceutical industry to fit her current role at ACMA.

Suzy is a mom, which is "probably one of the biggest things that has happened with [her] career." She had to learn to pivot with life changes, which is how she founded the Pharmacist Moms Group. In 2017, when Suzy was struggling with career/life balance, she formed the group which has now become the largest organization of women pharmacists in the country. It is now officially recognized as a 501-c-3. There are over 35,000+ members and also multiple subgroups of the Pharmacist Moms Group (PhMG). In 2018, Suzy started Women Pharmacist Day which is recognized annually on October 12. PhMG advocates for women in pharmacy and issues women face while working. Suzy speaks nationally across the country on topics related to Women in Pharmacy.

Hear more from Suzy and others by listening to her episode on the Talk to Your Pharmacist podcast or visit www.hillaryblackburn.com

Author, Tiny Life Changes - Lisa King, BSPharm

https://tinylifechanges.com/

Lisa King is co-author of "Tiny Life Changes," with her sister Lauren Daniels, who is a life coach and breast cancer survivor. The two sisters wanted to join forces and share what they have learned in their combined 45 years of health and healing. Their book, "Tiny Life Changes," went to No. 1 on Amazon on its launch date of Jan. 9, and Lisa and her sister Lauren are doing speaking engagements together and have put together a coaching and accountability package for women who want to change their lives. They believe that taking it one day and one step at a time will lead to big results and the achievement of goals and dreams. She loves sharing, especially with other pharmacists because she's been a pharmacist for about 30 years.

Lisa always knew she wanted to be a pharmacist. She married at a very young age, became a pharmacist, and started having children. She's always been a working mom and has always worked in community pharmacy. Her sister is a breast cancer survivor and founded an organization in Phoenix called the Happily Ever After League. Her sister had a very difficult time following her breast cancer diagnosis, and she had a double mastectomy when her youngest was only 11 months old.

The economic downturn of 2008 occurred at the same time, and she and her husband had a lot of real estate holdings and were going through a very difficult time as well.

Lisa and her sister provided support for each other through different difficult times in different ways by just becoming more positive. They delved into self-development, and from there wanted to share that with others - just how to turn around a difficult situation and to make it a little bit more positive, one day and one step at a time. This process is the basis for why they wrote the book, Tiny Life Changes.

Lisa is also the founder of Ditchbladderpain.com and is passionate about sharing step by step solutions for women to gain freedom from bladder issues. She has shared on various platforms about overactive bladder and painful bladder syndrome and the stigma that surrounds these bladder symptoms. Lisa has recently left community pharmacy and is currently a pharmacist in a patient care services pharmacy specializing in medical foods.

Hear more from Lisa and others by listening to her episode on the Talk to Your Pharmacist podcast or visit www.hillaryblackburn.com

Founder of Birth Control Pharmacist - Sally Rafie, PharmD, BCPS, APh, NCMP, FCCP
https://birthcontrolpharmacist.com/

Sally Rafie is an experienced clinician, researcher, educator, and advocate. In 2016, Sally founded Birth Control Pharmacist, an organization that provides education and training, implementation assistance, resources, and clinical updates to pharmacists prescribing contraception and key stakeholders, as well as leading and stimulating advocacy, research and policy efforts to expand the role and realize the potential of pharmacists in reproductive health and justice.

Sally received her pharmacy degree from the University of California San Francisco School of Pharmacy in 2008 and completed residency training at UC San Diego Health, where she continues to serve as a pharmacist specialist today.

Sally's passion for providing reproductive healthcare emerged early in her pharmacy training. She spent a summer in pharmacy school making outreach phone calls to hundreds of pharmacies to encourage them to prescribe emergency contraception under a new statewide protocol and then created a novel rotation for herself in reproductive. This same hunger to get more involved as a direct provider led to her crafting novel residency experiences. Sally started doing research on pharmacist roles in contraception care and serving as an advocate or advisor with various public health organizations. Even in these early stages of her career, Sally collaborated inside and outside the pharmacy profession, making a special effort to involve students and open doors for them.

Prioritizing professional development, Sally attended conferences and workshops and obtained certifications. Sally heartily accepted opportunities to fill administrative and leadership roles at work and in professional associations. Her first leadership position was in the American College of Clinical Pharmacy Women's Health Practice and Research Network as Public Policy Liaison, which led to being elected to serve as Chair position. She also became involved with her local San Diego County Pharmacists Association and rose to the President position.

Although Sally thoroughly enjoyed her work with medication safety and care in inpatient and ambulatory clinic settings at an academic health system, she continued her efforts in advancing access to contraception and pharmacist roles in reproductive healthcare. Sally found her niche – she has come to be nationally recognized as a thought leader in reproductive healthcare by pharmacists and has helped pharmacies gain recognition as an important access point for this care. As California passed the first legislation that allowed pharmacists to prescribe contraception, Sally assisted the Board of Pharmacy in drafting the protocol. When Sally then realized there was a need for expertise in advocating for and implementing this novel pharmacist service nationwide, she founded Birth Control Pharmacist to centralize these efforts. Expansions in pharmacist scope of practice allowed her to start a private practice, The Pharmacists Clinic, to provide direct care and access to services in her community.

Thousands of student pharmacists, pharmacists, and other healthcare professionals have been reached through Sally's teaching and training to provide patient-centered care, in turn caring for many more patients. She continues to precept and mentor students across the country, made possible with virtual rotations and collaborative research projects. Sally looks forward to contributing to health equity and realizing both the potential of pharmacists in providing care and community pharmacies as access points to care.

Hear more from Sally and others by listening to her episode on the Talk to Your Pharmacist podcast or visit www.hillaryblackburn.com

Founder and CEO of Your Pharmacy Advocate - Jerrica Dodd, PharmD, MS

https://yourpharmacyadvocate.com/

Dr. Jerrica Dodd is a pharmacist, entrepreneur, coach, and leader.

She holds a Doctor of Pharmacy degree from Florida Agricultural and Mechanical University, a Master of Science in Pharmacy Administration from The Ohio State University, and a Master of Science with a focus in Applied Pharmacoeconomics from the University of Florida. She completed her pharmacy practice and administration residency at The Ohio State University Medical Center.

Dr. Dodd has been a pharmacist for 22 years and transitioned into full-time entrepreneurship after a 17-year career in the pharmaceutical industry in multiple roles within Medical Affairs (medical information and medical science liaison). She has also managed a hospital pharmacy and has experience in retail pharmacy.

Her recent educational pursuits have been the completion of a Nutrition Health Coaching Certificate from the Institute of Integrative Nutrition. Currently, she is enrolled in the Institute of Functional Medicine and aiming to introduce a functional medicine perspective to the management of member patients of Your Pharmacy Advocate, LLC where she is the founder and CEO. Dr. Dodd has spoken on many stages across the country and is the proud Executive Editor of PharmaSis Magazine; Celebrating Women in Pharmacy.

Dr. Dodd enjoys traveling, reading, teaching Zumba, cooking, and attending cultural events. Jerrica spends the majority of her professional time traveling, speaking, consulting patients, and coaching women pharmacists to pivot in their careers and to build the life of their dreams. Her motto, "Your Dreams Are Urgent" is a call not to ignore the dreams and passions that make life worth living! This is why the focus of her publication PharmaSis Magazine is to feature women pharmacists who are building the life of which they dream! You can find her online as the guest for several podcasts that speak to pharmacists, women, and entrepreneurs.

With her background in pharmacy, leadership training, and her passion for people, Dr. Dodd enjoys encouraging people to be their best and to get the most out of every opportunity that life presents. Her favorite scripture is Luke 12:48: "to whom much is given, much is required" and Dr. Dodd endeavors to live life giving back from the abundant ways in which she has been blessed.

To learn more from Jerrica and others, listen to her episode on the Talk to Your Pharmacist podcast or visit www.hillaryblackburn.com

Principal Consultant at North Star Medication Optimization, LLC - Molly Ekstrand, BPharm, BCACP, AE-C

https://medicationoptimization.com/

Molly Ekstrand is currently running her own consultant firm called North Star Medication Optimization, LLC. Previously, she led the medication management program at Park Nicollet Health Services in Minneapolis, Minnesota. Her team of 11 pharmacists has on-site presence in 75% of the primary care sites reaching over 5,000 unique patients each year. Ekstrand practiced comprehensive medication management in internal and family medicine clinics for over 12 years, in 2 different health systems. She understands how fully to utilize a pharmacist in a team-based care model. When asked, how should pharmacists should approach that team-based mentality? Molly shares the following analogy about team-based care:

> "Why would you want a baseball team full of pitchers? All the people on a baseball

> team know how to bat, they know how to throw the ball. But they all have their certain spots on the field, and they all play a specific role. As we think about our different care team members, we have to think about the different skill sets that they have, the different training that they have, and the different perspectives they have from where they are on the baseball field, for example, and how can we play together in that environment? It's really important that we have to offer something unique and different, that no one else on our healthcare team can offer. And that's when we're going to be successful."

Molly advises that before the pharmacy profession can excel in adding to quality and cost solutions in healthcare, we must first get a seat at the table. She suggests starting conversations so you can understand the priorities of the people with whom you want to partner. Do some research on the different ACO and value-based purchasing models. It's really helpful to read publications on what other pharmacist colleagues have done, but we must keep in mind that it may not be the solution to a problem that your partner, or your future partners, don't have. Pharmacists do a great job of promoting pharmacists within pharmacy, but we need to branch out and promote ourselves to the greater public, whether that's with patients and policymakers or whether that's with our healthcare colleagues as well.

Molly is very passionate about pharmacy and how pharmacy and pharmacists, medication optimization, can really fit in to the value-based area. As we evolve into alternative payment models with so much focus on medication related health outcomes, she has a passion for working with other health care professionals to show how the profession of pharmacy is evolving. She also enjoys precepting future pharmacists, peer mentorship, and mentoring junior colleagues.

To learn more from Molly and others, listen to her episode on the Talk to Your Pharmacist podcast or visit www.hillaryblackburn.com

Founder of Functional Medicine Pharmacists Alliance - Lauren Castle, PharmD, MS

www.FMPhA.org

Lauren Castle, PharmD, MS, is the founder of the Functional Medicine Pharmacists Alliance (FMPhA), whose mission is to integrate pharmacists into the practice of Functional Medicine, and Functional Medicine into the profession of pharmacy. She completed her Doctor of Pharmacy from Ohio Northern University and her Masters of Science in Functional Medicine and Human Nutrition from the University of Western States. Lauren also works as a Market Health and Wellness Director for Walmart and serves as a social media influencer as @DrLaurenCastle on LinkedIn, Facebook, and Instagram.

Lauren found her way into functional medicine as she helped her husband with some nagging physical issues. Her husband had a lot of sinus and digestive issues and other things that they were trying to figure out what was happening. It seemed that over the counter remedies and those types of treatments, never really solved that problem. But a functional medicine approach seemed to alleviate those symptoms as they worked to discover the root cause of those issues. And in his case, they were able to determine through some testing that he had a gluten sensitivity.

After that experience, Lauren felt as if functional medicine was the future of medicine and something that she really wanted to learn more about. She researched several different programs that were out there, but ultimately since functional medicine was so new, she selected a program that was more structured and carried a recognizable designation - a masters degree. This pursuit fit in really well with her personal career goals since she knew wanted some type of secondary degree.

Lauren did not do a residency after her PharmD program at Ohio Northern, and thus was already seeking out that level of education. Finding the masters program at the University of Western States was the perfect fit for her since she knew that the type of larger companies that she'd been working in would appreciate that level of expertise versus perhaps a certification or health coaching program. However, Lauren says not everyone needs a masters degree in nutrition or in functional medicine which is one of the reasons that she started the Functional Medicine Pharmacist Alliance. As she started learning this information at her program, Lauren also started doing speaking engagements and getting out there and spreading the word about functional medicine through different pharmacy conferences at Ohio and Michigan pharmacist association meetings.

To learn more from Lauren and others, listen to her episode on the Talk to Your Pharmacist podcast or visit www.hillaryblackburn.com

Founder of The Public Health Pharmacist – Christina Madison, PharmD

https://www.thepublichealthpharmacist.com/

Dr. Christina Madison is the Founder and CEO of The Public Health Pharmacist, PLLC, a public health consulting firm. She is currently an Associate Professor of Pharmacy Practice at Roseman University of Health Sciences College of Pharmacy where she practices as a clinical pharmacist specializing in public health with a focus on infectious communicable diseases. Her public health consulting business, The Public Health Pharmacist, PLLC, is currently helping individuals and businesses navigate the COVID19 global pandemic, providing Public Health Solutions for getting businesses back in action, as well as providing expert public health and communicable disease commentary to major news outlets being feature in 50+ on-air TV appearances since the beginning of the pandemic. She has an intimate knowledge of the impact public health messaging, policy, and legislation can have on communities.

In 2004, Christina obtained her PharmD degree from the Roseman University of Health Sciences formerly known as the University of Southern Nevada. She then completed a pharmacy practice residency at the New Mexico VA Health Care System and obtained the Pharmacy Based Immunization Delivery Certification before becoming an Immunization Trainer in 2008. She also became credentialed with the Academy of HIV Medicine (AAHIVP) in 2013. Christina was elected Fellow of the American College of Clinical Pharmacy (FCCP) in 2018 for her service to the organization and contributions to the profession of pharmacy.

Dr. Madison has held several leadership roles throughout her pharmacy career. Starting out her career teaching at an Osteopathic Medical School as an Assistant Professor of Basic Sciences - Course Director Pharmacology with Touro University – Nevada, College of Osteopathic Medicine. After leaving her first faculty appointment, obtained another teaching position as an Assistant (2007-2013) then Associate Professor of Pharmacy Practice (2013- Present). She has also been involved in the training of other allied health professional trainees including medical students and residency as an Adjunct Clinical Associate Professor Department of Internal Medicine, University of Nevada School of Medicine (2015-2018). Her dedicated to moving the profession of pharmacy forward through service to professional organizations has included holding positions such as President (Nevada Public Health Association) – one of two pharmacist in the country to hold this position from 2013 – 2014, Chair (American College of Clinical Pharmacy (ACCP) Women Health Practice Research

Network (PRN)) from 2013-2014, and Chair - California Society of Health System Pharmacists (CSHP) Continuing Pharmacy Education Committee (CPE) from 2016-2017. Dr. Madison's commitment to community service through leadership in non-profit organizations and advisory board positions includes B.E. A S.H.E.R.O. Foundation (Executive Board Member) A Non-Profit Organization Helping Women and Girls in Vulnerable Situations (2019- Present), Boomer Naturals - Wellness Advisory Board Member – (full service wellness and personal protective equipment (PPE) company) (June 2020-Present), and Pills2Me – An On-Demand Medication Delivery Service (Advisory Board Member) (May 2020- Present). Advocating for public health and the profession of pharmacy to improve the health and wellness of vulnerable populations and the underserved is her passion and mission.

Her motto in life has always been "don't let the perfect be the enemy of the good." She typically says yes first and asks questions later. Christina acknowledges that, "so often we see professional women waiting until they meet the exact requirements for a job before applying because the want things to be 'perfect'." However, she has realized that opportunities will come when things aren't "perfect" and you have to embrace the "messy yes." Christina shares that being able to advance and fully leaning-in to your full potential is creating your own luck - when hard work and preparation meets opportunity. Taking a leap of faith may be the best decision you ever make.

When looking for a job, Christina advises that it's just as important to know what you don't want in a job as what you do want. If you don't see the position that is your dream job, create it. She used to be afraid of failing but realized that she could learn from those experiences and apply those lessons to future successes. Christina shares that being an entrepreneur is one of the scariest and best decisions she has ever made. She attributes all her past leadership positions which prepared her for the moments where she is now the one making all the decisions in her role as a founder and CEO.

To learn more from Christina and others, listen to her episode on the Talk to Your Pharmacist podcast or visit www.hillaryblackburn.com

Co-founder of Honeybee Health — Jessica Nouhavandi, PharmD

https://honeybeehealth.com/

Jessica Nouhavandi, PharmD, is the co-Founder and co-CEO of Honeybee Health, an accredited online pharmacy serving tens of thousands of patients across the country. Jessica founded Honeybee Health alongside her partner, Peter Wang, to serve the millions of patients who are underinsured or uninsured. She created a unique pharmacy business model that purchases generic prescription medications directly from FDA-approved wholesalers, cutting out middlemen (such as insurance companies, pharmacy benefit managers, etc.) and passing those savings along to patients.

The daughter of two working class immigrants, Jessica Nouhavandi, was the first one in her family to go to college. She earned her bachelor's degree in bioethics before becoming a Doctor in Pharmacy from Western University of Health Sciences. As part of running an online pharmacy, Jessica has helped Honeybee Health recieve its license in 41 states and territories (with 20+ personal licenses).

Before Honeybee, Jessica worked as a traditional retail pharmacist at a small, independent pharmacy in Southern California. One day, a patient walked in for a standard cholesterol medication. Jessica looked up his insurance, submitted his claim, and his copay was $90 which the patient couldn't afford. The number seemed wrong to Jessica as this was a generic, standard medicine that had been around for years. Curious, she looked up the out-of-pocket cost of these pills (aka the cost if you don't go through insurance), and it was $2. That's when Jessica realized that the traditional pharmacy model was broken; it prioritized profits, not patients. Insurance companies and other industry middlemen had artificially elevated prices at the cost of patients.

In addition to Honeybee, Jessica fights hard to change the healthcare industry on the highest level. She works one-on-one with legislators, senators, and congressmen and women to educate them on the struggles currently facing Americans when it comes to healthcare costs. She has taken on an even more public role during the COVID-19 pandemic to advocate for safer pharmacy access and help recently unemployed patients across the country continue to receive their life-saving medications.

To learn more from Jessica and others, listen to her episode on the Talk to Your Pharmacist podcast or visit www.hillaryblackburn.com

CEOs, VPs, and Leaders of Associations

CEO of Academy of Managed Care Pharmacy - Susan Cantrell, BSPharm, CAE

https://www.amcp.org/About/Leadership/AMCP-Board/Susan-A-Cantrell

Susan Cantrell is the CEO of the Academy of Managed Care Pharmacy (AMCP), which is the organization representing practitioners managing medication therapies. Susan took over as CEO in February 2016 and has a longstanding history in the association space as she was previously with ASHP for 19 years of her career. Susan is a University of Mississippi School of Pharmacy alum and was the very first pharmacy practice resident at the University of Mississippi Medical Center. She practiced pharmacy at University of Mississippi Medical Center after the residency and then took advantage of an opportunity when there was growth in the home infusion industry to work in that space. She was in specialty pharmacy before specialty pharmacy was an industry. Her work in associations has taken up most of her career and she has a real passion for it. Susan sees how she can serve a profession and how important associations could be in really advancing the work of their members. It's a turn that Susan hadn't anticipated when she went to pharmacy school several years ago, but she's happy to be there, especially at AMCP for the last couple of years.

Additionally, Susan is co-author of two books: Letters to a Young Pharmacist: *Sage Advice on Life and Career from Extraordinary Pharmacists* and *Letters from Rising Pharmacy Stars: Advice on Creating and Advancing Your Career*. It was her love of working with student pharmacists and aspiring pharmacy leaders that led her to come up with the idea for these two books.

Hear more from Susan by listening to her episode on the Talk to Your Pharmacist podcast or visit www.hillaryblackburn.com

CEO of American Association of Colleges of Pharmacy - Lucinda Maine, PhD, RPh

https://www.aacp.org/article/lucinda-l-maine-phd-rph

Lucinda Maine, PhD, RPh, serves as Executive Vice President and CEO of the American Association of Colleges of Pharmacy (AACP). As the leading advocate for high quality pharmacy education, AACP works to develop strong academic scholars and leaders to support excellent professional doctoral and postgraduate degree programs and to build relations with key constituency groups both inside and external to the profession of pharmacy. Prior to assuming her current role, in July of 2002, Lucinda served as the Senior Vice President for Policy, Planning and Communications with APhA, the American Pharmacists Association. Lucinda is a pharmacy graduate of Auburn University and received her doctorate at the University of Minnesota. She then served as a faculty member on the University of Minnesota's team, where she practiced in the field of geriatrics and was an Associate Dean also at the Sanford University School of Pharmacy. She has been active in leadership roles both in and out of the pharmacy profession. Prior to joining the APhA staff, she served as speaker of the APhA House of Delegates and as an APhA trustee. She currently serves on the Board of Directors for Research America and is an executive committee member of the American Foundation for Pharmaceutical Education. She's been honored with several prestigious awards, including the University of Minnesota's Outstanding Alumnus award, the Linwood Tice Friend of APhA/ASHP award, and the Gloria Niemeyer Frankie Leadership Mentor award from APhA. In March 2019, Lucinda received the Remington Honor Medal, which is the pharmacy profession's highest honor presented annually by APhA.

Lucinda has been at AACP for the last 16 years which has been the perfect combination of the earlier components of her career - half of which were in pharmacy education and half of which were in association management. She started in pre-pharmacy at Auburn early in the '70s and really never looked back from that point forward. Lucinda became very engaged in pharmacy associations as a student and then consistently throughout the early component of her career. She had two faculty positions: one at Minnesota, where she received my PhD, and one at Samford University in Birmingham, Alabama. In 1992, she left academia and joined the staff of the American Pharmacists Association, where she worked for 10 years. And so she spent about 10 years in academic pharmacy, 10 years in association management, and when they called to ask if she might be interested in the AACP position, she said, 'Well, you know, maybe on that balance, I'm well prepared to lead pharmacy's education association.'

To learn more from Lucinda and others, listen to her episode on the Talk to Your Pharmacist podcast or visit www.hillaryblackburn.com

EVP of Tabula Rasa HealthCare; President of the American Pharmacists Association 2021-2022 - Sandra Leal, PharmD, MPH, CDCES, FAPhA

https://www.linkedin.com/in/slealrx

Sandra Leal, PharmD, MPH, received her PharmD from the University of Colorado and completed a residency in Southern Arizona with the Veteran's Affairs (VA) system. She has extensive diabetes education training and started her career at El Rio Health, which is a federally qualified health center in Tucson, Arizona. Now, she is the Chief Executive Officer at SinfoniaRx, and Executive Vice President for the Health Plan and Payers Business Unit for Tabula Rasa HealthCare.

Although Sandra went to the University of Colorado, she wanted to move back home to Arizona where her family lived and ended up relocating to Tucson. She did a residency at the VA which she really loved and had a passion for ambulatory care pharmacy, since she really liked working with people and managing conditions. When the opportunity opened up for working at El Rio, she enjoyed being able to develop a clinic and design it in the way that she was taught at the University of Colorado where she had trained at some of the Kaiser clinics with some of the pharmacists being very hands-on with patients, managing their chronic conditions like diabetes and hypertension. The VA in Tucson had a very similar model with a lot of pharmacists integrated into primary care. So, the clinic that she started at El Rio was designed in that same way and was the first site to receive collaborative practice authority from the state of Arizona. They were able to initiate prescriptions based on those collaborative practice agreements, and Sandra stayed in that position for 14 years before moving over to SinfoniaRx in January of 2015.

Sandra enjoyed patient care but went into public health because she kept seeing the same kinds of problems - access and affordability issues and trouble navigating – related to the healthcare system. She decided to obtain her Public Health degree and focus on being able to address some of those systematic issues, policy changes, and then bring a scaled solution so they could see more people and manage conditions because they were seeing such an influx of people with pre-diabetes and diabetes, and more and more challenges with that. At SinfoniaRx, Sandra continues to replicate those efforts. When she joined SinfoniaRx, Sandra joined as Vice President for Innovation to replicate the models that she was developing at El Rio Health on a more national scale, and then using the resources that SinfoniaRx provides with their clinical call centers to be able to scale the services and replicate the impact pharmacists were having on the treatment teams and more importantly, the patient. Note: Tabula Rasa HealthCare acquired SinfoniaRx in 2017.

To learn more from Sandra and others, listen to her episode on the Talk to Your Pharmacist podcast or visit www.hillaryblackburn.com

Vice President of Professional Affairs at American Pharmacists Association - Anne Burns, BS, RPh

https://www.linkedin.com/in/anne-burns-453a023/

Anne Burns serves as Vice President of Professional Affairs at American Pharmacists Association (APhA), which is the largest pharmacy association in the country representing every part of the profession. In this role, Anne is responsible for the Association's strategic initiatives focused on advancing pharmacists' patient care services in team-based care delivery models, as well as payment for pharmacists' services, collaboration with other health care practitioner organizations, and health care quality. She leads the Association's practice initiatives on pain management and the opioid crisis and also works on APhA's medication management, medication safety, Health IT, and credentialing and privileging programs in addition to other key pharmacy practice issues. She has served on many medication management, opioid, and quality-related advisory councils.

Anne shares that her background and roots are in community pharmacy practice. In the early 1980s, she practiced in an independent community pharmacy in a medical office building, which provided excellent perspectives on caring for patients, being on the frontlines, and working with physicians and other health care providers. These experiences created a foundation that has informed her work throughout her career. Anne served on the faculty at The Ohio State University (OSU) College of Pharmacy for 13 years before coming to APhA. Anne joined APhA's Education Department in 1997 and transitioned to the Professional Affairs Department in 1999 to focus on pharmacists' patient care services and community pharmacy residency program accreditation. She is a graduate of OSU and completed the Wharton Executive Management Program for Pharmacy Leaders.

Anne loves teaching and working with student pharmacists and residents, and is energized by the opportunity to network with, and learn from innovative and dedicated pharmacists across the profession. She integrates these learnings in providing education and information to both pharmacy and external stakeholders, and in advocacy for the value of pharmacists in improving medication use and health outcomes. Anne is passionate about the need for a consistently applied patient care process, sustainable business models, health care information interoperability, and meaningful quality measures for pharmacists' services, and works collaboratively to further those aims. Anne's role as a caregiver for a chronic pain patient over the last few years has also significantly impacted her understanding of the challenges patients and their caregivers face in navigating the healthcare system and the roles pharmacists can play to assist.

Personally, Anne adores her family and enjoys the outdoors, especially scuba diving. She's even done some non-technical mountain climbing, which has helped to push her to take more risks.

To learn more from Anne and others, listen to her episode on the Talk to Your Pharmacist podcast or visit www.hillaryblackburn.com

Strategic Planning Manager at Aetna, a CVS Company; former VP of Clinical Operations at Axial Healthcare - Stacey Grant, PharmD

https://www.linkedin.com/in/stacey-grant-5a275750/

Stacey Grant, PharmD, has served as the VP of Clinical Operations at Axial Healthcare in Nashville, TN. Axial Healthcare is a healthcare technology company with solutions for health plans, providers and patients in the pain and opioid use disorder and behavioral health space.

She explains that "there's so much information out there, but the key is taking that information and making it actionable and giving it greater utility than as it sits in raw form."

Axial works with health plans to analyze data and then stratify patients based on risk. Axial also works with providers to educate them on the evidence-based prescribing practices and give them tools so that they have kind of at their fingertips ready access to this more actionable information. As Stacey says, "when you can drastically improve the lives of patients and save the healthcare system millions of dollars, that's kind of a no-brainer."

Stacey received her PharmD from the University of Tennessee and completed a residency with the Tennessee Pharmacist Association before joining PharmMD, a Medication Therapy Management (MTM) company. Stacey has lived in Tennessee for the past 15 years, most recently in Nashville. And the healthcare technology space is one that she has always found really exciting and intriguing, and where she has spent the majority of her career. Stacey serves on the Tennessee Pharmacists Association's Legislative and Policy committee, of which Stacey has formerly chaired. Stacey shares that "the committee has been really fun and a really good experience in advocacy and policy making, which is not one there's a lot of exposure to necessarily but is eye-opening when you think about healthcare in general and who's making the decisions and how those decisions are influenced. There's a huge opportunity there for us, as pharmacists, to influence that policy making, especially as it relates to healthcare."

To learn more from Stacey and others, listen to her episode on the Talk to Your Pharmacist podcast or visit www.hillaryblackburn.com

SVP at Sentry Data Systems - Lisa Scholz, PharmD, MBA

https://www.linkedin.com/in/lisa-scholz-pharmd-mba-fache-b3009111/

Lisa Scholz, PharmD, MBA, has had a career spanning community pharmacy, health system operations, government association management and technology solutions. She is currently the head of Industry Relations at Sentry Data Systems, a 340B health information technology vendor.

She is a pharmacist by training and background but is a self-professed nontraditional pharmacist - meaning she stepped outside of the box of what people think of pharmacy and has undertaken an adventure way outside of pharmacy and landed in the technology space. Lisa has extensive experience in operating and understanding the 340B program, a federal program that requires drug manufacturers to provide outpatient medications at a discounted price to eligible safety net providers – covered entities. Having this niche experience has provided numerous opportunities for her from leading consulting for the program to working in advocacy to her current position today.

Lisa was born and raised in Houston, Texas. As a native Texan, she never, ever thought she would leave Texas let alone Houston. Yet, she found herself having lived in Washington, D.C. for the last 10 years and more recently fleeing the snow and living in the great state of Florida. She loves Florida because she loves beaches and relaxing. Most would never know that because she is 150 percent in her work. When she gets a chance to relax on the weekends, she spends her time vegging out on the beach and reading leisure books and reading management books or books on how to just be a better person - she "sharpens the saw every weekend."

To learn more from Lisa and others, listen to her episode on the Talk to Your Pharmacist podcast or visit www.hillaryblackburn.com

---

Academia and Pharmaceutical Industry

Medical Science Liaison (MSL) for AstraZeneca Pharmaceuticals; Veteran United States Air Force; Top Ten Finalist and Talent Award Miss Veteran America 2016 - Kelby Kuhn, PharmD

https://www.linkedin.com/in/kelbykuhn/

Pageants might not generally make you think about pharmacy school, but as a pharmacy doctorate student Kelby was able to represent Roseman University of

Health Sciences College of Pharmacy and her future profession well. While in her doctorate program she participated in the Miss America Organization, earning many scholarships. She was a top ten finalist at the Miss Utah 2014 Pageant and received the Miss America Community Service Award, Miss America Academic Award and the Sadie Huish Memorial Scholarship. Kelby says she is often asked the question, "How did your military career begin?" While in my 1st year of pharmacy school a recruiter for the Air Force came and spoke to our class and talked about health professions scholarships. Kelby thought, "WOW, this sounds like a great opportunity, I can serve my country and pay for my education." The application for the F. Herbert Health Professions Medical Scholarship is very rigorous and competitive. Six months later, Kelby received a phone call informing her that she was one of two students nationally to be selected on an annual basis for the scholarship. She thought, "why not, I'm single, I love to travel and this is a great opportunity. It's one of the best decisions I've made."

Upon graduation from Roseman University of Health Sciences College of Pharmacy she was commissioned a Captain in the United States Air Force and assigned to the 59th Medical Diagnostics and Therapeutic Squadron at Joint Base San Antonio Lackland Air Force Base Texas. While there, Kelby served as the Chief of Clinical Support Pharmacy, overseeing one of the largest pharmacies in the Air Force managing a budget of $6.1 to 9.5 million, supervising twenty-six pharmacy personnel daily and dispense 51,000 refills annually.

Additionally, she was responsible for providing direct patient care to the Diabetes Center of Excellence and Anticoagulation Clinic, ensuring patient outcomes were met, while providing comprehensive medication therapy management and patient education. While serving in the Air Force, Kelby was able to have some unique opportunities. She was named Officer of the Quarter in only her second quarter of being on active duty. She continued to excel and was named Officer of the Year. Kelby was also chosen to film a recruitment video for the Air Force:
https://www.youtube.com/watch?v=EAtkVHfaw1A

Kelby was able to participate in the Miss Veteran America Pageant, where she was a Top Ten Finalist and Talent Award winner. She shares that, "the Miss Veteran America Pageant isn't just about serving our country; it's about being an advocate for the fastest growing population of homeless veterans, female veterans and their children. When you think of a veteran, the first thing you think of is a man. Women are often overlooked." She appreciated this opportunity to advocate for women who can't advocate for themselves. Kelby has devoted much of her life to community service, she has raised thousands of dollars for the Children's Miracle Network, and the Juvenile Diabetes Research Foundation. As an advocate for the non-profit organization Final Salute, an organization to help female veterans, Kelby has been instrumental in raising over $80,000 for these women and children. She also founded the "Wrapped in Love" Blanket Project, donating hundreds of blankets to the homeless. Additionally,

Kelby has completed two humanitarian medical missions to Guatemala. Kelby has already inspired many with her dedication and commitment.

Along with exemplifying the ideals of the Miss America Organization, Kelby's commitment to the Air Force's core values, of integrity first, service before self, and commitment to excellence has provided Kelby with a foundation for leadership, decision making and success no matter the level of the assignment, or the difficulty of the task. After 3 years of active duty, Kelby returned to Salt Lake City Utah, where she continues to serve her country as a member of the Utah Air National Guard. She enjoys spending time hiking and skiing the mountains of Utah with her husband and daughter. Currently Dr. Kuhn is a Medical Science Liaison (MSL) for AstraZeneca Pharmaceuticals, focusing on cardiovascular metabolic diseases. As an MSL, she has the opportunity to educate on the shared risk factors of cardiovascular, renal and metabolic diseases that are often not diagnosed or addressed and is committed to help change clinical practice, to address unmet medical needs and create a seamless disease management pathway for patients worldwide. Dr. Kuhn has a passion for developing collaborative relationships with medical experts and researchers to follow the science and push the boundaries of science to deliver life changing medicines while putting patients first.

To learn more from Kelby and others, listen to her episode on the Talk to Your Pharmacist podcast or visit www.hillaryblackburn.com

Professor of Pharmacy Practice at University of Arkansas for Medical Sciences; President of the American Pharmacists Association 2018-2019 - Nicki Hilliard, PharmD, MHSA, BCNP, FAPhA

https://www.linkedin.com/in/nicki-hilliard/

Nicki Hilliard, PharmD, MHSA, BCNP, FAPhA, is a professor of pharmacy practice at the University of Arkansas for Medical Sciences (UAMS) College of Pharmacy. She received her PharmD from UAMS College of Pharmacy and a Master's in Health Services Administration from the University of Arkansas at Little Rock.

Dr. Hilliard has pharmacy practice experience in community pharmacy and free medical clinics but has focused most of her career to becoming an innovative educator of nuclear pharmacy practice and management. Nicki is a former APhA-APPM President and an APhA Trustee and has served on APhA's Government Affairs, Strategic Planning and Policy standing committees. She has also served on the Board of Pharmacy Specialties and is the current chair of the Pharmacy Provider Status Task Force and the Government Affairs Committee for the Arkansas Pharmacists Association. She clearly has a lot of great leadership role experience.

Nicki shares that her personal life and her career seem to be intertwined because she loves her work and gets to meet so many different pharmacists around the country, so she considers them her pharmacy family.

To learn more from Nicki about some of the biggest initiatives that she planned as APhA's President in March of 2018, check out her episode on the Talk to Your Pharmacist podcast or visit www.hillaryblackburn.com.

Professor and Associate Dean of Administration and Operations at University of Colorado Skaggs School of Pharmacy and Pharmaceutical Sciences - Laura Borgelt, PharmD, MBA

https://www.linkedin.com/in/laura-borgelt

Laura Borgelt, PharmD, MBA, is a Professor and the Associate Dean for Administration and Operations at University of Colorado Skaggs School of Pharmacy and Pharmaceutical Science. She has over 20 years' experience in the departments of clinical pharmacy and family medicine and serves in an active role for strategy development and implementation in academia. Laura received her BS in pharmacy at the University of Iowa and her PharmD at the University of Colorado-Denver, and she "went back to school" to complete her Executive Masters of Business Administration at the University of Colorado in 2019. She completed an ambulatory care specialty residency with the University of Colorado in Kaiser Permanente Rocky Mountain Division.

With an emphasis in women's health and patient safety, she has published more than 100 articles and a textbook entitled, "Women's Health Across the Lifespan." She has provided presentations to nearly 100,000 people to local, national, and international audiences. Laura has led or served on more than 40 local, national, and international committees, including task forces for the state of Colorado, focused on education of students, academic affairs, leadership, and health.

Laura especially loves speaking with other women about their health and wellness, especially some "tough" topics including contraception, menopause, sexual health, and … life. She believes that every woman can be empowered through knowledge to be an action-based advocate for their own health and well-being. Laura lives this out on a daily basis through her passion for swimming, triathlon, meditation, and personal growth. She also has three young boys, 11, 13 and 15 years.

To learn more from Laura and others, listen to her episode on the Talk to Your Pharmacist podcast or visit www.hillaryblackburn.com

Professor and Interim Chair, Department of Pharmacy Practice at Lipscomb University College of Pharmacy – Dr. Kamala (Kam) Nola, PharmD, MS, FAPhA

https://www.linkedin.com/in/kam-nola-24a72a14/

Dr. Kamala (Kam) Nola, PharmD, MS, FAPhA completed her Doctor of Pharmacy degree from the

University of Tennessee (UT) College of Pharmacy and her Masters of Science in Pharmaceutical Sciences in Health Outcomes and Pharmacoeconomics from the UT College of Graduate Health Sciences. While working on her masters, she completed a two-year residency with Bartlett Prescription Shop and the Veterans Affairs Medical Center in Memphis, Tennessee.

Her career in pharmacy education began as a Clinical Assistant Professor at Mercer University Southern School of Pharmacy, and Kam is currently Professor and Interim Chair, Department of Pharmacy Practice at Lipscomb University College of Pharmacy in Nashville, Tennessee. As an educator, Dr. Nola is passionate about student engagement with the most vulnerable and underserved in the Nashville Area and beyond. Through her course in *Pharmacy Management of Vulnerable & Underserved Populations* and partnership with the Lipscomb University College of Pharmacy APhA-ASP Chapter, she has forged community partnerships with close to 30 community organizations such as YMCA, YWCA, Nashville Cares, Rescue Mission, Room in the Inn, Faith Family Clinic, Arthritis Foundation, Bellevue Foodbank, etc.

Dr. Nola started her career as a leader in the Tennessee Pharmacists Association (TPA)/Tennessee Society of Student Pharmacists and American Pharmacists Association (APhA)-Academy of Students of Pharmacy (ASP). Since then, she has served as a former TPA President and Associate Executive Director. Kam has represented Tennessee pharmacists as a House of

Delegates member for APhA several years. Additionally, Kam is active in the APhA Care of Underserved Patients Special Interest Group (SIG) and other SIGs.

An active AMCP member, Dr. Nola specializes in payment and reimbursement for pharmacists in order to improve access for patients. She is recognized by the American College of Rheumatology (ACR)/Association of Rheumatology Professionals (ARP) for her advocacy efforts on behalf of patients, practice, and the specialty. In 2009, she served on the APhA/Academy of Managed Care Pharmacists (AMCP) Bridges to Partnership Advisory Council on Managed Care and Community Pharmacy. In 2011, she was awarded the Ann Kunkel Advocacy Award, the highest recognition for advocacy work by rheumatology professionals. She holds the honor of being the <u>first</u> pharmacist elected as President of the ACR/ARP and as an Executive Committee and Board Member of the American College of Rheumatology. Since her time in leadership, the number of pharmacists in rheumatology practice has grown tremendously. There are now physicians who stand up before their peers and say "they cannot practice without a pharmacist."

Her leadership, advocacy, and practice has benefitted the profession, her patients, Tennesseans, as well as a national and even international influence. Dr. Nola represented rheumatology health professionals in European Union with the European Union League Against Rheumatism (EUALR) to develop collaboration between health professionals on both continents. She has been an advocate for recognition and training of rheumatology professionals in countries that have poorly developed educational processes. In addition, she has advocated for greater pharmacist engagement with EULAR.

As a former UT community pharmacy resident, she has constantly advocated for community pharmacy practice even when not working in the area of practice. Her community residency project and graduate thesis, "Evaluation of a Lipid Management Program in Community Pharmacy" was the first program in Tennessee to show the value of pharmacist engagement in direct patient care. The work was used to aid in the updating of the Tennessee Pharmacy Practice Act revisions in the mid-1990s. She continues to promote diabetes, pulmonary, heart disease/stroke, arthritis, and medication therapy management at the community pharmacy level.

Other significant contributions that Dr. Nola has had on the profession include working collaboratively with the Tennessee Medical Association, Tennessee Dental Association, Tennessee Nursing Association, and Tennessee Hospital Association to build consensus on the basics required for medication reconciliation and development of a Universal Medication List for Tennesseans. She also worked to promote involvement of pharmacists in improving patient care through public health initiatives through work with the Tennessee Department of Health Heart Stroke Committee, Tennesseans Improving Patient Safety, and the Tennessee Arthritis Action Plan. Dr. Nola has a talent for voicing the needs of patients, populations, providers, the profession, student pharmacists, and faculty.

Her favorite quote, “The attitude you take into any given situation ultimately determines its outcome” is paraphrased from Viktor E. Frankl’s *Man’s Search for Meaning.* Her leadership philosophy that of a servant leader, and she models that compassionate care to her students, faculty, and staff. Dr. Nola’s leadership brings a breadth of experience, passion, compassion, and commitment to pharmacists and future generations of pharmacists on a daily basis.

Chief Pharmacy Officers (CPOs) & Hospital Leaders

Executive Director, Population Health Pharmacy Solutions at Banner Health - Melissa Duke, PharmD, MS, BCPS

https://www.linkedin.com/in/melissa-skelton-duke-72080931/

Melissa (Missy) Skelton Duke, PharmD, MS, BCPS, serves as the Executive Director, Population Health Pharmacy Solutions at Banner Health, a health system based in Phoenix, AZ. In this role, she is responsible for the design, deployment, and oversight of innovative pharmacy strategies that provide value to healthcare consumers, providers, and populations. This includes a variety of pharmacist-provided clinical services, population health management services, and patient advocacy programs. Prior to this role, Melissa led a comprehensive specialty and home delivery pharmacy programs for Banner Health. Additionally, Melissa led the development of acute care and ambulatory clinical pharmacy services at Intermountain Healthcare.

Melissa received a bachelor's degree in Microbiology from Arizona State University, a Doctor of Pharmacy degree from the University of New Mexico and a Master of Science in Pharmacotherapy Outcomes Research from the University of Utah. She completed a PGY1/2 Health-System Pharmacy Administration residency program at Intermountain Healthcare.

When Missy considers her career trajectory, she says "some of the most important elements of my career were not part of my original plan. Throughout my education, I learned about all the roles that pharmacists can take and all the ways that pharmacists can bring value to healthcare. My personal career decisions took me in a direction that I wasn't anticipating. It's been so much fun and that continues to be a theme throughout my career – most recently with my work in population health." One of the other key lessons that Missy has learned along her leadership path is the power of mentorship. She always coaches learners to "find people who are doing what you want to do, or who are like what you want to be like and develop relationships with those people." Missy credits many leadership lessons, honest feedback, networking opportunities, and many other career boosters to the mentors who came into this profession before her.

Missy is also very focused on giving back to the profession through active engagement in our professional associations at the state and national level. She has held a number of elected and volunteer leadership positions at the state and national level, including most recently being elected as the APhA Speaker of the House of Delegates. Additionally, she serves as a co-leader of the APhA Institute on Substance Use Disorders.

To learn more from Missy and others, listen to her episode on the Talk to Your Pharmacist podcast or visit www.hillaryblackburn.com

Chief Pharmacy Officer and Vice President of Medication Management for Ascension - Lynn Eschenbacher, PharmD, MBA

https://www.linkedin.com/chatin/wnc/in/lynn-eschenbacher-pharmd-mba-fashp-8381132?trk=people_also_view_2

Lynn Eschenbacher, PharmD, MBA, FASHP, is currently the Chief Pharmacy Officer (CPO) for Ascension and Vice President of Medication Management for Ascension and the PGY1 + 2 combined Residency Program Director. In this role, she leads the enterprise-wide strategic direction for all Ascension Pharmacy and medication management services across the continuum of care and system-wide. Her responsibilities include assessing external operational pharmacy industry trends and developments that represent risk and opportunities for the organization and developing short and long-term plans to respond to potential risks and to capitalize on opportunities. She is accountable for the implementation of medication management related short and long term strategic, financial and quality goals. She establishes strong collaborative relationships with key leaders throughout the organization and with pharmacy thought leaders across the country. Previous to this role, she served as the National Director of Pharmacy Operations for Ascension.

After obtaining a Bachelor of Science degree in biology from Indiana University in Bloomington, she attended the University of Texas at Austin to obtain her Pharm.D. degree. She then completed a pharmacy practice residency at Parkland Health & Hospitals in Dallas. Dr. Eschenbacher worked at Duke University Hospital as a clinical pharmacist, clinical coordinator and medication safety officer. Additionally, she completed her Master of Business Administration degree at the Fuqua School of Business at Duke University. She most recently was the Assistant Director of Clinical Services at WakeMed Health & Hospitals in Raleigh, North Carolina, and the PGY1 Pharmacy Practice Residency Program Director. Dr. Eschenbacher has received the Circle of Excellence award at WakeMed for Market Development and Quality Outcomes. She is also the ASHP Delegate for the Acute Care Forum in North Carolina, a past chair of the ASHP Section Advisory Group for Medication Safety, and past chair for the ASHP Section for Inpatient Care Practitioners. She received the 2015 ASHP Distinguished Service Award and is the editor of the ASHP Clinical Coordinator Handbook. Lynn has earned a Six Sigma

Black Belt and was a 40 under 40 award recipient from the *Triangle Business Journal*.

In her role as CPO, she has had the opportunity to testify in front of Congress during the House Energy & Commerce Subcommittee's hearing "Lowering Prescription Drug Prices: Deconstructing the Drug Supply Chain." Lynn shared her expertise to advocate for affordable, life-saving prescription drugs. Additionally, she presented to Office of National Drug Control Policy (**ONDCP**), which is responsible for developing, implementing, and assessing drug policy.

She has been married for 15 years and has 3 daughters (twins going into 7th grade and youngest going into 3rd grade). Lynn enjoys going for walks and bike rides with her kids, making up dances with the youngest, being a soccer mom, going on nature hikes and scavenger hunts, solving riddles, and playing with her children as much as she can. In her spare time, she also volunteers with her family in activities such as world hunger day, sandwiches at church, blessing bags, etc.

To learn more from Lynn and others, listen to their episode on the Talk to Your Pharmacist podcast or visit www.hillaryblackburn.com

CHAPTER 3

SUCCESSFUL ATTRIBUTES AND BEHAVIORS OF WOMEN IN THE WORKPLACE

Executive Material: Women's Strengths as Leaders

In modern organizations, especially those with multigenerational staff, women can be of great value. Women are generally more inclusive leaders that value the unique talents and skillsets of all workers, and they possess that ability to make their team feel valued.

What Exactly Is Executive Material?

Executive material is having that executive presence. It is walking into a room with command demonstrated by shaking hands with everyone and making eye contact. It is dressing the part of an executive officer, looking professional and put-together, because there's a saying that "you dress for the job you want, not the job you have." It is speaking confidently and decisively without raising your voice like a question at the end of a sentence, also known as upspeak. All of these things and more are ways that women can demonstrate they can lead. All these things and more are what makes a woman, or anybody executive material.

What Are the Strengths of a Leader?

Here is a list of several strengths according to various leadership books which apply to any leader, male or female:

- **Integrity** – This is doing the right thing irrespective of other factors. This is a foundational characteristic upon which the others should build.
- **Authenticity** – This refers to actions that are consistent with deeply held beliefs. You act with authenticity when your actions are in line with the beliefs you hold dear.
- **Communication** – This is having effective verbal and nonverbal communication. It is the ability to share information to others with all clarity.
- **Confidence** – This is the belief in one's abilities. Being confident allows you to trust in your capabilities without undermining what you can do.
- **Adaptability** – The ability to be resourceful in various situations and circumstances.
- **Humility** - Celebrating the wins of others. It is also being modest regarding your own importance and achievements.
- **Perseverance** – The stamina and endurance to stick with something for the long run despite difficulty.

- **Growth mindset** – The mindset of "I can" vs. "I cannot." Having the right mindset enables us to choose how we experience the world.
- **Emotional intelligence** – Leaders often have a high emotional intelligence meaning they can accurately perceive their own and other's emotions.

Examples of Tools to Evaluate Strengths

Women embarking on this journey to enhance their leadership skills should thoroughly reflect and assess their own leadership style and strengths. There are a variety of tools available for women to evaluate their strengths. As mentioned earlier in the book, some of my favorites include the Enneagram, Clifton Strengthsfinder, and DiSC profile. One of the personality tests that I most benefited from was Clifton Strengthsfinder. Clifton's StrengthsFinder encourages a focus and refinement of your strengths, rather than spending time making your weaknesses mediocre. However, a self-awareness of one's weaknesses is also needed to identify potential blind spots and areas of self-improvement. Hopefully, these types of personality tests confirm what you already know about yourself.

My top five strengths according to Clifton Strengthsfinder 2.0 (2007) include being an achiever, a maximizer, a learner, an individualist, and a competitor:

Achiever: Achievers are driven to perform at the highest level to accomplish their goals; most pharmacists are type-As and likely achievers as well. They typically thrive in a fast-paced environment where they can check things off their list. Striving for one's best leads to achievement and success; thus, one aspect of my leadership style is the desire to lead by example.

But this drive for perfection can be off-putting, especially to those not so motivated. I've found that it is okay to not take charge in every scenario, and that it's important to strike a balance between encouraging co-workers to achieve their personal best without taking on the entire workload myself in an effort to make it "perfect."

Maximizer: Maximizers are always making processes better and have an internal drive for quality improvement. In other words, they're often looking for ways to take something from being good to being great. These individuals thrive in work environments where the culture is not to settle for the status quo.

Recognizing others' strengths and ensuring that they are using their talents to the best of their ability leads to success for our company. It also encourages my co-workers that their talents provide a valuable contribution to their own success and the overall success of the company. This strength helps me to lead effectively as I strive to maximize both my strengths and those of my co-workers through collaboration.

Learner: Learners fully adopt the mantra, "never stop learning." To fulfill the Pharmacist's Oath, pharmacists "pledge to committing to a lifelong learning approach to provide the best care to our patients." This mantra helped get me through the Doctor of Pharmacy degree and the annual continuing education courses required to be a pharmacist. A passion for learning enables you to get up to speed quickly on projects or to assist with clearing any roadblocks that co-workers might encounter. Lifelong education is important whether it is through the pursuit of an additional degree like an MBA, even after being in the workforce for nearly ten years, or by reading books and articles to keep up to date in one's field. I've had a personal goal to read more books and subscribed to Audible to "read" (aka listen) to more books throughout the year; hence, my maximizer trait coming out as I "read" while driving, etc. Reading books was an instrumental part of my childhood and is a great way to continue that knowledge building throughout one's life.

Being a learner has given me the humility to accept that I may not always have the answer initially, but I can research and learn it to share that knowledge with others. Learners should understand that sharing the knowledge of how to do a given task is more important than doing it for someone. As a wise man once said: "Give a man a fish and you feed him for a day. Teach a man to fish and you feed him for a lifetime."

Individualization: Individualists excel at putting people into the best positions to help them to succeed. As mentioned in the book *Good to Great,* it is important to follow the concept of "first who, then what." If you are building a team, you must have the right people on the bus then the right people in the key seats to ensure they (and the organization) thrive. Individualists lead through knowing when, what, and to whom to delegate tasks and getting the right people on the right teams.

As the junior high and later high school cheerleader captain, I identified and organized the cheerleaders who were the best at jumps or dances or stunts; then, positioned them in a manner that each had the opportunity to shine individually as the squad excelled as a whole. I continue to use this individualization skill to learn about people and make meaningful connections based on their unique interests.

Our leadership team recently participated in a retreat that began with an intentional review of our leadership profiles to offer us a better understanding of each other. Individualists particularly enjoy learning about others' strengths and how to best interact with them and capitalize on their strengths. My team acknowledges this trait in me as they rely on me in various situations from serving as an organizer for planning events to finding the right speaker for special topics for our conferences.

Competition: Competitors pursue excellence and are always up for a challenge. They can push any team that they are on to be the best and bring others up alongside them.

This strength manifested early in my life as I strived to win every academic award in school, and ultimately the valedictorian spot in high school. Even now, I prefer group exercise classes where I can compare myself to others which pushing me to work harder. When selecting guests for my podcast, I choose well-spoken and accomplished colleagues whom I admire since hearing and sharing their stories inspires me to pursue bigger things in my own career.

What Strengths Do You Have?

How often have you heard during an interview or at least prepared for an interview with the question: "tell me your strengths and weaknesses." Not only will knowing your strengths help you prepare for interviews, but this awareness will help you learn what to focus on. Focusing on your strengths is a better strategy rather than improving your weaknesses to mediocrity, because it is through your strengths that you can make the biggest impact.

Leaders need to be self-aware of their strengths and those of their team. If you are the leader of an organization or department, encourage your entire team to take a personality test and share the results with everyone. This deeper understanding of others' differences and strengths is particularly helpful in team-based work. Our organization, Dispensary of Hope, had all our employees take the StrengthsFinders test which led to a deeper understanding of each other. StrengthsFinder describes in detail how to capitalize on your strengths and to identify strengths in others that work well with yours.

Taking the time to self-reflect is an important exercise. Use some of the tools mentioned numerous times throughout the book or do other self-reflection work or talk to trusted friends and advisors to give you honest feedback.

CHAPTER 4

CHALLENGES WOMEN FACE IN THE WORKPLACE

Women in the workplace often experience challenges such as facing harassment, not receiving due consideration, or being excluded from the boys' club. I'm sure that I'm not the only one who has experienced challenges in the workplace and will share some personal examples as these are important topics to cover. Lean In reports that "33% of women and 11% of men have seen or heard biased behavior toward women." Biases, whether conscious or unconscious, present challenges that affect women's daily work environment and ability to advance. Another challenge is that 54% of women have experienced some type of sexual harassment in the workplace as reported by an Inc. article (Zetlen, 2020).

In terms of harassment, I've been called "sweetie" or have been flirted with by customers when working in retail establishments as a pharmacist or earlier in my life as a waitress. Typically, I would let it roll off but if it continued, I would act more assertively to prevent it by being standoffish and not welcoming those advances.

I've had challenges with being a young leader and not being taken seriously. When I first got out of school, I had to work on my confidence to see myself as a peer with other more seasoned pharmacists. Now ten years into my career, I have finally built up the credibility (through time and experience) to see myself as an equal to any CEO, CPO, or any other leader at any level of an organization.

Then there is being excluded from the "Good Ole Boys club." In a meeting with the senior leaders at a large pharmacy organization, I was the only female in the room. That organization's COO did not acknowledge my presence by refusing to look in my direction during the entirety of the meeting. He looked towards and included the two men that I was with but never looked my way as if dismissing me. In another scenario, I had to bring in a colleague to speak "male to male" to "get through" to a few Good Ole Boy male pharmacists on a board of pharmacy when we were seeking approval for my company to be an approved program in their state.

There has been the misassumption by some that I was getting my MRS degree and would quickly "retire" upon having kids. During an interview with a future employer, the interviewer knew that I was newly married and made a comment about the hospital benefits which included being "a good place for a free baby" assuming that I was not going to be working long term and was already ready for kids.

Despite various challenges, I have continued to learn and grow without allowing any of those challenges to hold me back from continuing to strive for the pursuit of excellence and ultimately higher levels of leadership.

What Are Biases Against Female Leaders?

Men and women are different and so are their leadership styles. While women tend to be more democratic and participative in their style, men lean towards a more autocratic style. However, when women do operate with a more directive or autocratic style, they are viewed less favorably than men in the same roles (Eagly, 1992). This is something to consider as you move up the corporate ladder - you have to stay authentic to your own leadership style. If an autocratic style is not your way, then you don't adopt that style just because that's how a male might operate if he were in your position.

Men often receive recognition for their **professional** accomplishments while women often receive recognition for their **personal** accomplishments. Additionally, men get fewer negative feedback comments than women do on performance reviews according to Fast Company (2014). Women often get "dinged" for coming across as too harsh.

Female leaders sometimes hold biases against other female leaders. But not surprisingly, women are less likely than men to express their bias against other women (Catalyst, 2018). Women in executive positions have an obligation to encourage other women. They should consider this a call for awareness not to forget young emerging female leaders.

Reflection: What are the challenges that you've faced in the workplace as a woman? And how have you been able to overcome those challenges?

Are There Unwritten Rules for Career Advancement?

Networking: The very first on this list of unwritten rules for career advancement is networking. It's often said that your network is your net worth, and that building relationships is helpful to advance your career. However, I've often found that women are generally more reluctant to initiate lunch or coffee meetings with fellow female leaders; whereas my husband, for example, is on several lunch and coffee meetings weekly nurturing his network.

Use your sphere of influence to get you to where you want to go. Use your sphere of influence to connect and gain support from others. While many may say "pharmacy is a small world," being intentional with building and maintaining those relationships is important.

- How can you use your existing network to land your next job?
- How can you use your relational capital to increase your influence within a group or organization in which you are involved?

Confidence: Self-confidence is a level of self-assurance coming from an appreciation of one's own abilities and qualities (McKinsey, 2015). You develop self-confidence as a result of past leadership experiences and success. Women's self-confidence is often relational.

Confidence can be as important as competence in the workplace; however, women often struggle with feeling as confident as their male counterparts. This happens for a number of reasons, some being that:

- Women are often more humble than men.
- Women may experience "imposter syndrome," or self-doubt, more frequently than men and credit luck or some other circumstance for their success. This self-doubt may creep up internally and we have to work on changing our internal thoughts to quell that.

Navigating office politics: To succeed in the workplace, you must learn to navigate office politics. You will notice an emergence or increase in office politics during change such as when resources or power shifts. Certain factors that can increase politics at an organization include a financial crisis, a void in leadership, or the development of individual or coalition agendas.

There are ways to get things done in the workplace and often that means knowing who controls the decision-making process. Knowing "how things work" in your workplace is key to advancing and not fumbling your way through. Often these rules are unspoken and, therefore, never explained.

Women tend to keep their heads down and remain steadfast in the belief that hard work pays off for those promotions. What they often fail to realize is that politics can also play a role in the organogram, or structure and hierarchy, of many organizations. In order to thrive in an organization, knowing the types of people that get promoted and how people are promoted is essential. While many organizations are indeed meritocracies where those who work hard and produce results are promoted, disparities still exist in the promotion landscape. The Women in Workplace study by McKinsey (Lean In, 2020) showed that 72 women to every 100 men are promoted. At the top of organizations, the shift from merit to power which is the "real glass ceiling." It's important to learn how to play the game.

Negotiation: Negotiation is discussing or conferring with a view to reaching an agreement. If you've read Steven Covey's "7 Habits of Highly Effective People," you know the best-case scenario for negotiations is a win-win. How does one achieve a win-win situation related to salary?

Do women negotiate less? Yes. In the workplace, a typical negotiation between the employer and employee is over the salary. When you take a new job, one of the critical issues to cover in the job offer is the salary offer. Babcock (2003) finds that men make 7.6% more than women from the same graduating class because women don't ask about the salary; only 7% had tried negotiating. Women tend to underestimate their abilities and often don't apply for jobs until they feel 100% ready.

You never know what the answer will be unless you ask. And there's really no harm in asking. Women on average initiate fewer negotiations with their managers. This failure to "ask" can lead to significant lost earnings over their career.

Many women fear asking for what they want for fear of being tagged too brazen or too bold. But asking for that promotion or telling your boss about your goals are actually factors needed to succeed. Women usually don't speak up and ask for a salary increase and in fact generally ask for 30 percent less money than men do (Kay, 2014). This is incredibly important for that very first job because it can set the trajectory for a woman's pay in the future. If your first salary is lower than it should be, this fact may set you back for years going forward since raises at the same organization are often percent increases or if you change jobs, then your future employer may ask what your previous salary was. Another factor to consider regarding salary discrepancies is that women are more likely to leave the workforce than men to care for children.

What Are Ways that Women Can Advance?

From a personal standpoint, women can work to develop self-confidence, political savvy and negotiation skills. They should also be introspective to identify any potential internalized stereotypes.

How Can Women Better Navigate Office Politics?

There are a number of things women can do to navigate office politics in a better and more efficient manner. Women can incorporate strategies to enhance personal power and influence. They can create networks that are more entrepreneurial and diverse by seeking out new opportunities to connect with others. They can increase overall visibility by taking leadership roles. In addition, women can also engage in inclusive practices and strong mentoring relationships.

Connections and building relationships are pivotal in the pursuit of influence. Power is sometimes a push; influence is often a pull. While our position or title often reflects power, this power can also come from ourselves - our expertise, the image we offer, our relationships and connections. Thus, it is important to engage your networks and alliances. Stay visible and socialize with leadership to make yourself a peer. Continue to show respect for their executive position while demonstrating your self-confidence. Try to relate personally with them to create bonds. We must be insiders to change the rules.

How Can Women Work on Their Self-Confidence?

Nurturing provided by family and friends and other support systems from an early age can create a strong foundation that can bolster women's self-esteem making them more likely to try things, even if they fail. However, self-confidence is a trait learned through experience.

Women should practice self-promotion. For example, women are often humble and do not boast about their accomplishments, but sometimes it is helpful to remind others – especially your supervisor. I even tend to forget about what I've accomplished since my last performance review and have started a running list of accomplishments, so I am prepared during the next reviews and other discussions with my supervisor.

How Do You Ask for A Raise?

Women can be PROACTIVE and PREPARED by acknowledging two goals for negotiating: 1) issue/task goal and 2) relationship goal. Remember to convey why it makes sense for the organization or person you're trying to win over and look for win-win scenarios.

- Know what you want
- Know your BATNA (best alternative to a negotiated agreement)
- Don't accept the first offer
- Be creative in your ask
- Practice what you will say
- Balance empathy and assertiveness
- Keep the company the focus
- Anticipate the objections

The New York Times featured an article, "A Toolkit for Women Seeking a Raise," which is a great guide (Bernard, 2010). Additionally, the book Never Split the Difference by expert hostage negotiator, Chris Voss, is another great resource from which you can learn some tips. Just a few takeaways from this negotiation guidebook include:

- Pause and use the time you have to your advantage.
- Mirror the other person's mannerisms
- Label the emotion that is being experienced
- Use your name in negotiations to humanize. "The Hillary" discount
- Use how and what, not why. WHY puts people on the defensive.

How Can Women Support Other Women?

Our commitment as women to share with others the common barriers and challenges that we have faced is an opportunity to learn from each other. When colleagues use words with gender stereotypes like "she's too emotional," there's a chance for us to speak up. We can speak up for other women in our organizations and even find allies with whom to connect and share experiences. Finally, being a vocal champion for women is important in order to support and advocate for females in the office space.

If you are a leader, offer to mentor younger females. Or if you are pursuing a career in leadership, then find female role models who have chosen paths you hope to emulate.

What Can Organizations Do to Promote Women?

To make sure that women are prepared and confident to lead, they need mentorship and training to be ready for leadership roles. Organizations can implement formalized programs to cultivate and grow their pipeline of leaders.

- Know their talent pipeline of women
- Invest in building women's skills - especially resilience, grit and confidence (McKinsey, 2015)
- Ensure that respect is a key value integrated into the company's culture.
- Promote the same standards for both men and women during employee evaluations
- Provide sponsors and role models
    - Formal sponsorship programs help to open doors for younger females seeking to advance in their organizations.
    - Men and women who are senior leaders can commit to sponsoring top women talent.

Companies can create policies that support women. For example, they can promote awareness about these issues, such as disparities in pay. In 2018, women earned $0.82 to every $1 earned by men in annual earnings (Semega, 2019). In 2019, The U.S. Bureau of Labor and Statistics reported that women pharmacists made 84 cents to the dollar earned by male pharmacists.

Companies now have diversity targets requiring them to find, interview, and hire diverse candidates. More organizations are requiring quotas for women to sit on boards or have senior positions. In fact, France, Germany, India, Italy, and Norway already have quotas for any publicly traded company.

We must keep in mind that women achieve power by putting themselves out there and being visible and accomplished. Women are smart and tough, and we must continue to work hard and promote ourselves. Unlike most women in the 1950s-60s, the majority of us do work outside the home – often by necessity. We may no longer solely be caretakers and we've come a long way, but we still have a long way to go.

Reflection Questions

1. Think about a boss that you really liked.
   What were the characteristics that made him/her successful?

   How can you emulate those qualities?

2. Who is helpful to you? On the other hand, who is not supportive to you?

CHAPTER 5

INTEGRATING WORK AND FAMILY

Women often work hard to overcompensate. We worry that we're not measuring up or that people think we aren't getting everything done and that we're held to a higher standard for competency than men (Catalyst, 2007).

Women, especially high achievers, often lean toward overcommitting. We want to say yes even if it means taking on more than we can handle at a time for fear that we might miss an opportunity or look incapable. This could also be due to poor limit setting or "feeling bad" about saying no. Taking control of our schedules, aka our time, and learning to set boundaries are ways to stop saying yes to every request or potential opportunity.

Since motherhood can be a major contributor to lack of career advancement, more people are waiting longer than usual to have babies. When they do have babies, the Family and Medical Leave Act signed in 1993 will only guarantee your job for 12 weeks and that is unpaid leave.

Some short-term disability can kick in, which covers 6 weeks for a natural delivery or 8 weeks for a Cesarean section. The US is one of the only fully economically developed countries that does not offer paid maternity leave. Surprisingly, there have been no updates in this legislation in over 25 years. Yet many companies, like Google and other tech companies, are implementing longer maternity leave and even paternity leave policies. Companies' offering paternity leave helps to normalize taking time off for a new child or adoption, which is important regardless of gender.

Moving for a spouse's job may also be a factor in a woman's (or man's) career path. A few of the female pharmacists mentioned in this book are married to physicians and moved to different cities for their spouses' training or job. People have to do what is best for their family and moving for your spouse does not mean that the females' dreams are put aside but may in fact open the door for other opportunities in new cities.

How Do You Find Balance?

Women can have families AND be CEOs at the same time or even hold other leadership positions. To do this, women have to be intentional and they need a strong support system alongside a supportive spouse. Sometimes this might even mean taking a break to focus on family for a season and being the CEO of their household.

Taking a break from their careers does not mean that women cannot continue to develop skills that are transferable or that they cannot return to a career that has an upward trajectory. They can even take on other roles of leadership to practice their leadership skills like being involved in civic organizations or possibly in their children's school as room mothers during seasons where they might take a step back from their career.

Returning to work or continuing with work after children is absolutely doable. Women generally become more efficient at work, but they often struggle with how to be 100% both at work and at home. Surrounding themselves with resources, a good support system, and resetting expectations is necessary.

At the writing of this book, I am expecting our first baby and honestly delayed having a family to pursue my career and enjoy being married for five years. While I am not an expert on motherhood, hopefully in a few years I will have more perspective to provide on this topic and how to find "balance."

Pharmacy is a great career for females – likely why so many women have decided to choose a career in pharmacy. It offers flexibility and a variety of career options. Personally, I loved being finished with my school within six years (2 years of pre-pharmacy before entering pharmacy school as a junior in college) as compared to my medical school colleagues who require eight years, then at least three years of a residency. The profession also offers women the chance to earn great incomes to contribute financially to their families, even while working PRN (as needed) or a few days a week.

What Can Organizations Do to Support Women Balancing Family Life?

Like Google and some other companies in the tech industry that I have mentioned earlier, companies don't have to wait for legislation to create better family-leave policies. Organizations can ensure that their environments are conducive to expecting and new moms.

In 2010, the Fair Labor Standards Act (FLSA) required organizations to provide a private, safe and clean space for new mothers to pump. They can also make sure that there are places for pregnant women to rest or take a seat during the period of their pregnancy. This is especially important in the retail pharmacy setting where pharmacists are often standing during shift periods of about 8 hours and sometimes do not have the time or even a chair, to take a seat. Women that stand for long periods of time are at an increased risk of going into early labor.

Companies can also foster family friendly environments. This is equally important for both men and women. Leaders in companies should model talking about their families, asking questions about their employees' families, and they should develop the ability of being able to understand the position of employees who need to take off for a sick child or need to attend an important school function or event. A healthy workplace environment could also mean making more work-from-home options available or even flexible work arrangements for employees.

Reflection Questions

1. Success looks like ______________________________ to me.

2. I need to do ______________________________ to achieve this success

3. When successful, I will be able to

   ____

4. Reflect on one mindset that has prevented you from accomplishing a goal. Now think about how a different mindset could help you accomplish that goal.

CHAPTER 6

DEFINING OWN YOUR LEADERSHIP STORY

To become a leader, you must believe that you are one. How do you conduct yourself in the world? Do you see yourself as a leader? You might be asking yourself, "How do I lead when I'm not in charge?" Authors Andy Stanley and Clay Scroggins have an excellent book titled just that, "How to Lead When You're Not in Charge." In the book, they advise aspiring leaders to be good stewards of what they are in charge of even if it's just your desk at your office or your room/garage at home.

Being a young aspiring pharmacist can be overwhelming. You might be thinking "where do I begin?" since there is often not a clearly defined pathway for leadership. Hopefully, learning about some of the career paths of the women featured in this book will inspire those younger females on taking their first step towards leadership. However as mentioned when referencing the book *How to Lead When You're Not in Charge*, leadership doesn't always come with a position or title. Leadership is more about what we do for good and how we use our influence.

How Do You Define Your Own Success?

Success tends to look different during different seasons and in different circumstances. Having children may change a woman's priorities. Maybe you might want to take some time off to be a full-time mom, if your financial situation allows it. Or maybe you might look for another position that allows for more flexibility to be at-home for longer periods with your children as opposed to having a demanding schedule or one where you had to travel or work every other weekend.

When you were fresh out of school, maybe you were figuring out what you wanted to do. Once you figure that out, you might not want to take time off or go part time. Perhaps you love working and your current job and that's great. You should not feel guilty for working and being a working mom role model for your daughters.

My career path has taken some unexpected turns along the way. I remember taking some questionnaires during pharmacy school about my preferences to help better understand and think through what my priorities might be for my career. A flexible work schedule was a priority for me since I enjoy socializing with friends and traveling, thus having to work every other weekend was not something that I wanted to do. Being with family and friends and doing things that I love, such as being outside and travelling make me happy. To me, happiness is a choice that often starts with being grateful. Finding a career that makes you happy is important, and the great thing about a pharmacy degree is that with over 100 different career paths, you can always change what you're doing if you don't like it!

My path has changed several times over the past ten years from the hospital/ambulatory setting to independent pharmacy to a health plan and mail order pharmacy. From all of my past experiences: pharmacy school, residency training, and different pharmacist roles, I picked up transferrable skills which help support the work that I do currently while continuing to "grow" my skill set. These experiences, and my innate relational and networking skills, have culminated in my current role which is a "nontraditional" role as the Director of Pharmaceutical Services at Dispensary of Hope, a charitable medication distributor. This was a role that did not exist before I started in this position, and my volunteering led to this unique opportunity.

Volunteering for the Dispensary of Hope certainly opened a door of opportunity. As the Director of Pharmaceutical Services, I am responsible for providing clinical pharmacist expertise to support the organization as well as its network of pharmacies and charitable clinics. This includes leading our research and formulary development and create tools for successful program utilization by the pharmacies and charitable clinics in the Dispensary of Hope network. My work with health systems includes strategy development for identifying and implementing programs to address gaps in pharmaceutical care through inclusion of the Dispensary of Hope program and consulting with pharmacy leaders across the country to share expertise on affordable medication access for low income patients. In addition to these clinical responsibilities, I also utilize my relational skills to develop and maintain strategic partnerships with several external organizations including The Advisory Board Company, Research Triangle Institute, and Belmont and Lipscomb Colleges of Pharmacy.

For pharmacists who are interested in alternative career paths, that space is growing. As you can see from the wide variety of women featured, a pharmacy degree truly prepares you for just about anything - critical thinking skills, ability to research, taking complex information and simplify it. My predictions for some of the biggest areas of pharmacy practice for the future will be in pharmacogenomics, ambulatory settings to help with the shortage in primary care, and telepharmacy delivered services. Find what interests you and define your success in that!

How Do You See Yourself as a Leader?

I've been blessed to work for an organization with a CEO who calls us to be leaders. He speaks to our identity and encourages others' strengths. He calls them leaders, even when people may not have a title.

Often, you might feel powerless without having a title which suggests you are in charge. Or perhaps, you might feel like an unlikely leader believing you don't have the skills, experience, or what it takes. But as God has called unlikely leaders such as Gideon, who was not a soldier or the biggest in his family but who was actually hiding from his enemies, we too can be unlikely leaders when we are called by others.

How Do You Define Your Leadership Vision?

My vision for the future is to create a community for women in pharmacy who are in the pursuit of leadership roles or want to pursue leadership roles. I have worked towards that vision first through building a podcast that highlights others' leadership stories, including both males and females.

Your vision must align with your values. My vision for women pharmacy leaders aligns with my values of supporting and encouraging others and pursuing excellence. While the vision is the hopes and dreams for the future, a mission statement defines what a company (or individual) does and how they do it.

Leaders must be rooted in strong values to make good, consistent decisions. A good leader often exemplifies ethical leadership which is defined by values such as trust, honesty, and integrity. The CEO of my organization frequently advises that a good litmus test when making decisions might be: "Would you like this to be on the front page of a newspaper? Or would you still like the person in the mirror after this decision?"

Recently, I had the opportunity to meet former Tractor Supply CEO, Joe Scarlett, who shared with everyone at our dinner a copy of their company's mission statement. Joe gave a compelling story on the importance of instilling their company values into their team so they can make decisions and better perform their jobs. A woman working in purchasing of animal supplies for Tractor Supply recognized that one store was selling significantly more iodine than any other store. Upon some digging, she discovered that the store was in an area with a lot of drug issues and that iodine was used in the production of methamphetamine. After contacting manufacturers about other product alternatives, she made the decision to switch from iodine to another product that was not used in drug production. This employee didn't have to ask permission, because she felt empowered to make the decision by following Tractor Supply's values which emphasized the importance of ethics. Ultimately, this story filtered up to the CEO as a powerful example of his team understanding and embodying his company's values and they celebrated her doing the right thing.

How Do You Share a Compelling Message?

Leaders must present a compelling and consistent message at all times. Successful businesswoman Carly Fiorina shared in a 2003 Fortune interview that her recipe for success included: speaking to people as individuals, speaking about what matters, and believing what you are saying in both your head and your heart. You can't persuade people if you don't believe in what you are saying. You must display confidence and assertiveness. There are a few ingredients that make a compelling story: a positive vision of the future, inspiring core values, and engaging and inclusive leadership style, emotional intelligence, and courage (Bilimoria, 2005).

Dave Ramsey advises in his book **EntreLeadership** the importance of selling in that "because leading involves persuading a team to follow you, people who know how to sell often end up leading." In fact, the whole company is in sales – particularly those in direct customer service. Customers who have a good experience will remain customers and even may serve as a referral for your company. Southwest Airlines is consistently used as an example of a company that has great customer service, mainly because the founder Herb Kelleher, like the CEO of Tractor Supply that I mentioned earlier, promotes in the employees the company's vision that they only hire people that can fit their core values of fun, passion, service, family, hard work and engagement.

Overall, your compelling message much like an "elevator speech," must project your leadership vision. A key hallmark of transformational leadership is the ability of leaders to convince and encourage others of the vision of the future (Khan, 2016). Leaders should be able to simply communicate the vision and strategy to the team (Montgomery, 2018). If that vision is not clear, then the followers will not follow. Casting a clear vision to employees is necessary in achieving organizational goals and to draw others to a higher purpose and calling.

How Do You Want to Be Known?

Start with the end in mind is sage advice and Habit 2 in Stephen Covey's "7 Habits of Highly Effective People." This principle encouragers readers to visualize themselves at your own funeral – a bit morbid, yes, but a helpful exercise – and think about what people will say about you. Covey's advice to have a clear vision of your destination because knowing where you want to be will help guide how you need to get there. As mentioned earlier, a compelling vision not only guides you but also leads your team, like a compass, in the right direction. Developing a personal mission statement based on your values can help you to discern what things you should do or not do in life or your career.

Standing by your values as a leader helps your team to know where you stand. When your decisions are based on principles, your team can set their expectations on how you will react according to those principles and be reassured by the stability that provides. Employees need consistency from their leaders. When you're the boss, you have to watch coming off as having a bad day often because it puts everyone else on your team on edge. Employees need stability from their leaders.

Reflection Questions

1. What are your values as a leader?

2. Make sure your values align with your goals. Know your why. This drives your purpose!

3. Watch Simon Sinek's TedTalk (inspirational speaker series) or read his book "*Start with Why*" to consider your why as you consider your calling.

4. What is your legacy? What do you want people to remember you by? Think of former coworkers or those whom you have supervised – how do you want them to remember you? What do you remember most about them?

CHAPTER 7

PURSUING YOUR CAREER GOALS

While not everyone envisions himself or herself as a leader or has aspirations of climbing the ladder at their organization, hopefully this book encourages people to do so. This book profiles several women that have been successful and can serve as role models for other ambitious women who want to pursue leadership positions or unique career paths.

This book also identifies several resources and concepts that have particularly made an impact on me. While I didn't go into depth in each of these areas, readers can seek out topics depending on their own interest level and situation. Consider these references a "preview" into a much deeper personal and professional development area. I strongly encourage you to take time to ponder and complete the Reflection sections in these last few chapters.

Why Pursue Leadership Positions?

Observing role models, or leaders, to aspire and study to learn from specific examples of what worked and didn't work for them. You may identify well-known leaders or a local leader in your own organization to observe which could be accomplished by reading a quote or article about them on a regular basis. You may be thinking, "How can I decide which leader to study?" To solve for this, you can engage other more experienced leaders at your organization to help narrow down from their list of recommended leaders or inquire which well-known leader most resonates with them. Studying successful leaders can mold us into better leaders as we adopt what we learn to our own leadership style.

Pursuing Additional Skills or Certifications

Healthcare professionals often have several credentials at the end of their name. How do you decide what is relevant or not? It depends on your goals.

Residency. For the past several years, completing a PGY-1 residency has become a natural next step upon graduation from pharmacy school. Many wanting to stay in hospital pharmacy continue their training with a PGY-2 to specialize and ensure they can secure positions in highly desired settings such as critical care or ambulatory care. While these trainings don't necessarily add another credential, they do provide great experience to better equip the newly graduated pharmacist for clinical practice by honing those skills for an additional year or two under highly trained mentors.

BCPS. Another common certification that many pharmacists will pursue is one available from the Board of Pharmacy Specialties (BPS). BPS reports there are over 26,000 pharmacists with the Board Certified

Pharmacotherapy Specialist (BCPS) or generalist credential, but they also offer over ten other options including oncology, pediatric, including nutrition support. If you are wanting to practice pharmacy in the hospital or ambulatory care setting, it is recommended to obtain one of these BPS certifications – especially, if you are in a competitive market.

Masters Degrees (MBA, MPH, etc). Adding a masters degree such as a Masters in Business Administration (MBA) or Masters in Public Health (MPH) can be helpful for those who have a particular interest in business or public health. Choose a program based on your goals and to fit your lifestyle and budget. There are benefits of doing online or in-person degrees based on factors such as flexibility, cost, university prestige, or networking opportunities.

Additional credentials and degrees can help boost your existing PharmD degree. They can give you confidence and even a leg up when applying for job opportunities. Several of the women featured in this book have gotten additional degrees, whereas others have relied on the versatility of their PharmD.

Taking Opportunities

A common theme from many of the female leaders' stories is their willingness to seek and take opportunities. This is also true for my leadership story even during my internship days on Capitol Hill which led to my pharmacy experience at the Health Resources and

Services Administration's (HRSA) Office of Pharmacy Affairs in Washington, D.C. I didn't know what the Office of Pharmacy Affairs did, but I took the chance and it provided a great background on federal programs and caring for underserved populations which I now use in my current role. The willingness to take chances often opens doors to new career opportunities.

Finding Your Niche

Another theme seen in many of the female leaders' stories is that each has found a niche, or a particular field within pharmacy to excel. For example, Lauren Castle became passionate about functional medicine while researching how to better treat the root cause of some medical issues that her husband was experiencing. Lisa Scholz capitalized on her background in the 340B program to make several career moves within that specific niche.

Becoming an expert in a topic requires 10,000 hours according to Malcolm Gladwell's book, Outliers. Having this level of expertise supports one's confidence in themselves, as well as others' view of you!
With so many different career paths available for a pharmacist, picking a niche can be a tough choice. As you try to identify your niche or calling a few questions to consider include: Who's in my network? What does the world need? What makes me cry? Jim Collin's book *Good to Great* describes this introspection as the Hedgehog Concept as a guide to that decision based on three factors: 1) what are you passionate about 2) what

can you be the best in the world at and 3) what best drives your economic engine.

What does it take to be "great"? To me, anyone who uses his/her talents and gifts to the best of their ability qualifies; greatness involves knowing that you are doing the best you can possibly do and setting a good example for others to follow to help them achieve their best as well. It is a pursuit of excellence; my high school motto was in fact, "excellence with all your heart."

Being a Team Player

A common theme from many of the female leaders' stories is their focus on being a team player. Healthcare is, in fact, team-based care. As a leader, it's important to build a good team – those who have similar values to you and those with different skills. Using screening tools as mentioned earlier in the book can help ensure that you've got a diverse team. For example, having a representative from each of the DISC profiles is helpful for balance.

How you treat your team, or coworkers, matters. Dave Ramsey encourages the use of the term team member instead of employee because terminology matters. He wants people to feel like they are part of something bigger, that they play a role. Generally following the "Golden Rule" of treat others how you want to be treated is good advice whether you are interacting with family, friends, or coworkers.

It's often said that "pharmacy is a small world." Thus, you never know when a former classmate or preceptor may be your future boss or vice versa! It's always best to be a team player and build great relationships with others because you never know when you might want an "in" at a potential employer.

Setting Goals

While setting goals is step one, you must take actions towards goals to make progress. Writing the goal down, setting calendar reminders or having an accountability partner are all ideas of ways to have a tangible goal to work toward.

As I was pursuing my MBA in 2019, my mission was to clarify, develop and improve my leadership ability and skills so that I could continue to make meaningful contributions in my current position and look forward to advancement with more responsibility and influence. Women can accomplish their missions by selecting SMART (Specific Measurable Achievable Realistic Timely) goals.

Here is an example of a SMART goal that I selected during my MBA coursework:

A goal that I would like to accomplish is to recognize and empower others by writing one note of encouragement per week to a member of my team throughout this MBA program. I can measure this goal by writing a note weekly and gaging feedback from the recipients. This goal is attainable since it is within my capacity to set a 15-minute reminder on a weekly basis to write a note. This goal is relevant because it will help me to better engage my team members and lift them up. Being able to look outwardly at my team at their successes further refines my individualization skills.

A potential obstacle in obtaining this goal might be trying to decide which team member and what achievement to recognize each week. To solve for this, I can create a checklist of each employee's name and specifically write to one every week. Additionally, I will be attuned to noticing their accomplishments. With twenty-four other employees at my office, I can accomplish this task within 6 months.

As you are considering how to pursue your career goals, I encourage you to identify SMART goals. Another great practice that Zig Ziglar and many other great coaches recommend is to set goals in each key area of one's life including: career, financial, spiritual, physical, intellectual, family, and social areas. Then conduct a personal performance review at the end of each year to determine how well you progressed towards those goals. Each January, I set goals for the year as well as look at my 5 and 10-year goals.

Tim Ferriss teaches "Dreamlining" or what would you do if you couldn't fail? Ferriss recommends that people think about the five things that you dream of having, being, or doing - or what you could fail in each. Think about your goals for the next 5, 10 and 20 years, then write that down. Dreams that are written down become goals and goals can become a reality.

Setting goals and challenging myself has been a core theme of my life. For instance, my pharmacy classmate and I decided during our P4 year that we would run our first half marathon. Once I committed to this goal, I was going to accomplish it, even when my classmate backed out during the summer before our October race. If you've never done a half marathon, I encourage you to do just one. The Team in Training program that supports the Leukemia and Lymphoma Society (LLS) provides a great opportunity for you to have a team (others who are also committed to the race). By committing to run the race, you are also signing up to fundraise over $2,000 for LLS. I did this through a letter writing campaign – so everyone knew that I was running in this race! It was an awesome experience and I have since run another half marathon since moving to Nashville for the St. Jude Rock 'n Roll Marathon when my now husband paced me.

Growing up my goal was always to pursue a career in medicine so that I could use my academic talents to the best of my ability, as well as fulfill my desire to serve others. As a pharmacist, I have been challenged academically and have had a way to help others. I've tried to be a leader in my community by continuing to be involved in organizations like the Nashville Junior League and Nashville Ballet, as well as serving on numerous committees for pharmacy associations.

Have I achieved all the goals? I'm not sure; there will always be some other goal to pursue. When does one truly know when they have met all their milestones or what else their life and career may hold in the future?

As I get ready for motherhood, my perspective will likely change how I am achieving and pursuing excellence.

Additionally, I have included the below questions to assist you in pursuing your career goals. The questions are in the line of personal and professional development alongside leadership and influence.

Personal Development

Are there specific areas that are you are lagging in?

Recommendations:

Take a Coursera course in that area. To prepare for this book, I took a course titled "Women in Leadership: Inspiring Positive Change" offered by Case Western Reserve University.

Read books on leadership. One of my personal favorite books on mastering personal leadership by developing successful habits is Steven Covey's "7 Habits of Highly Effective People." Covey teaches principles that anyone can implement for personal growth. Buy this book now!

Are there opportunities that you can take to gain new skills?

Recommendations:

Volunteer. I found my current role because I had been volunteering there. The organization had never had a pharmacist on staff and finally had the funding to hire one. Luckily, I already had the relationships there and was on the shortlist to interview for the position.

Shadow or interview those people who are in positions that interest you. The book "*Designing Your Life: How to Build a Well Lived, Joyful Life*" by Bill Burnett and

Dave Evans offers a great guide for how to approach these people to interview. This book emphasizes the connection between - who you are, what you believe, and what you are doing. It's very important that your work life and your personal life be in harmony. "Designing Your Life" means to think like an architect – to create the life that you want. This book suggests that you design your life much like an architect designs a house, and to envision three different scenarios of what your future five years from now might look like.

Professional Development

Do you have a mentor(s) that you can ask career advice from – preferably someone not in your company? Do you have a sponsor, someone in your company, who can advocate on your behalf for promotions and added responsibilities?

Recommendations:

Seek mentors and serve as a mentor to other people that look up to you.

- Identify 2-3 people who can help you achieve your goals
- Help others achieve their goals. The true test of leadership is if you've passed it on to others to carry on.

In summary, what pieces of advice do we offer to other women pharmacists?

- Ask for what you want
- Do not downplay your accomplishments. Be proud of your hard work. Show off your confidence.
- Negotiate. Ask for promotions - if you have earned it.
- Define your own success.

Passing It On

I've always tried to follow Luke 12:48: "From everyone who has been given much, much will be demanded; and from the one who has been entrusted with much, much more will be asked." I believe that we must use our God given talents to His glory and to give back to help others.

A goal of mine for making a difference and giving back to the profession has been to inspire, engage, and connect with pharmacists across the country. I am a motivator and a coach by default, and I enjoy leaning into my natural talents of networking and cheering others on. With this book, I hope to start a new chapter focused on equipping and preparing women to feel confident taking on leadership positions and building a community to support existing female leaders. As you embark on your leadership journey, remember DePree's (1989) guidance that "Leadership is an art, something to be learned over time, not simply by reading books." Go out and practice!

REFERENCES

Chapter 1

1. Bilimoria, D., (2012). Inclusive Leadership: Effectively Leading Diverse Teams, Leadership Excellence, 13.
2. Brown, F. W., & Reilly, M. D. (2009). The Myers-Briggs Type Indicator and Transformational Leadership. *The Journal of Management Development, 28*(10), 916-932. doi:http://dx.doi.org.wgu.idm.oclc.org/10.1108/02621710911000677
3. Catalyst, Inc. 2020 Mar 13. Women on corporate boards: quick take. Available from: https://www.catalyst.org/research/women-on-corporate-boards/
4. Cummings, G., Midodzi, W., Wong, C., & Estabrooks, C. (2010). The contribution of hospital nursing leadership styles to 30-day patient mortality. *Nursing Residency,*59(5):331-9. https://doi.org/10.1097/NNR.0b013e3181ed74d5
5. Ely, Ibarra & Kolb. (2013).Women rising: the unseen barriers. *Harvard Business Review*.
6. Luce CB, Hewlett SA, Kennedy JT, Sherbin L; Center for Talent Innovation. The power of the purse: engaging women decision makers for healthy outcomes. talentinnovation.org/_private/assets/PopHealthcare_ExecSumm-CTI.pdf. Published 2015. Accessed July 1, 2020.

7. Rotenstein LS. (2018, October 1). Fixing the gender imbalance in health care leadership. Harvard Business Review. Retrieved from: https://hbr.org/2018/10/fixing-the-gender-imbalance-in-health-care-leadership
8. Sherwin B. (2014, January 24). Study: why women are more effective leaders than men. Business Insider. Retrieved from: https://www.businessinsider.com/study-women-are-better-leaders-2014-1
9. Paustian-Underdahl S, Walker LS, Woeher D. (2014). Gender and perceptions of leadership effectiveness: a meta-analysis. *American Psychological Association*, 99(6), 1129-45.
10. U.S. Bureau of Labor Statistics. (2019). "Table 3: Employment Status of the Civilian Noninstitutional Population by Age, Sex, and Race, 2018," *Current Population Survey*.
11. Women Leadership and Twenty-First Century Challenges. (n.d.) Retrieved from: https://www.alliant.edu/blog/women-leadership-and-twenty-first-century-challenges#:~:text=Studies%20by%20Alice%20Eagly%20of,motivates%20followers%20to%20improve%20performance.

Chapter 3

1. Babcock L, Lashever S, Gelfand M, Small D. (2003, October). Nice girls don't ask. Harvard

Business Review. Retrieved from: https://hbr.org/2003/10/nice-girls-dont-ask

2. Bernard TS. (2010, May). A toolkit for women seeking a raise. New York Times. Retrieved from: https://www.nytimes.com/2010/05/15/your-money/15money.html?pagewanted=all&_r=1
3. Catalyst, Inc. 2018. Men (and women) are biased against women. Available from: https://www.catalyst.org/2018/12/13/men-and-women-are-biased-against-women/
4. Catalyst, Inc. 2010. Unwritten rules: why doing a good job might not be enough. Available from: https://www.catalyst.org/research/unwritten-rules-why-doing-a-good-job-might-not-be-enough/
5. Davis, K. (2014). The One Word Men Never See In Their Performance Reviews, Fast Company. Available from: http://www.fastcompany.com/3034895/strong-female-lead/the-one-word-men-never-see-in-their-performance-reviews
6. Eagly A., Makhajani M., Klonsky B. (1992). Gender and the evaluation of leaders: a meta analysis. *American Psychological Association*, 111(1), 3-22.
7. Kay, K. & Shipman, C. 2014. The Confidence Gap, The Atlantic, http://www.theatlantic.com/magazine/archive/2014/05/the-confidence-gap/359815/
8. Lean In. 2020. Women in the workplace 2019. Available from: https://leanin.org/women-in-the-

workplace-2019?gclid=EAIaIQobChMI9o_2g-Pj6gIVRtbACh25MQmnEAAYASAAEgLJGPD_BwE
9. Narrow the Gap. Available from: https://narrowthegap.co/gap/pharmacists#:~:text=Women%20pharmacists%20made%2084%20cents,down%2011%20cents%20from%202011.
10. Semega J, Kollar M, Creamer J, Mohanty A. "Table A-7: Number and Real Median Earnings of Total Workers and Full-Time, Year-Round Workers by Sex and Female-to-Male Earnings Ratio: 1960 to 2018," *Income and Poverty in the United States: 2018* (United States Census Bureau, September 10, 2019): p. 46.
11. Yee L. (2015). Fostering women leaders: a fitness test for your top team. McKinsey. Available from: https://www.mckinsey.com/business-functions/organization/our-insights/fostering-women-leaders-a-fitness-test-for-your-top-team
12. Zetlin, M. (2020, Apr 23). 54 percent of women report workplace harassment. How is your company responding?: the wrong approach to sexual harassment can lead your company to lawsuits, or a visit from the feds, Inc. Available from: https://www.inc.com/magazine/201804/minda-zetlin/sexual-harassment-workplace-policy-metoo.html

Chapter 5

1. Catalyst, Inc. 2007. The Double-Bind Dilemma for Women in Leadership: Dammed If You Do, Doomed If You Don't, Available from: http://www.catalyst.org/knowledge/double-bind-dilemma-women-leadership-damned-if-you-do-doomed-if-you-dont-0

Chapter 6

1. Bilimoria, D. & Godwin, L. (2005). Engaging People's Passion: Leadership for the New Century. In Ronald R. Sims & Scott A. Quatro (Eds.) Leadership: Succeeding in the Private, Public, and Not-for-Profit Sectors, Armonk, NY: M. E. Sharpe, Inc., Chapter 14, pp. 260-279.
2. Cummings, G., Midodzi, W., Wong, C., & Estabrooks, C. (2010). The contribution of hospital nursing leadership styles to 30-day patient mortality. *Nursing Residency,*59(5):331-9. https://doi.org/10.1097/NNR.0b013e3181ed74d5
3. Khan Z., Nawaz, A., et al (2016). Leadership Theories and Styles: A Literature Review. *Journal of Resources Development and Management*, 16, 1-7.
4. Montgomery, A. (2018) "Transformational Leadership Style: 7 Lessons for Developing Leaders." Executive Master of Leadership, USC Price, https://eml.usc.edu/blog/transformational-leadership-style?utm_campaign=Leadership%20Style&utm_medium=email&_hsenc=p2ANqtz--

q_g31__w21_D8Kya1hA32rO28uAGv-DWRR77_trinz6RPAfNTMm3_F72OP1vl-AzwVwVmvExN2MtCHEdBi5BPPj0bqCfqD6m1vT8LJt_5c87hcHw&_hsmi=62942899&utm_content=62942899&utm_source=hs_automation&hsCtaTracking=8378d77b-3b30-43c3-8dd2-0b533fb5c4bd%7Ce0701014-96d3-4ef2-a1cd-86d52435bd93
Accessed June 1, 2020.

5. What is the enneagram? (n.d.). Retrieved from: https://www.truity.com/enneagram/what-is-enneagram
6. DiSC Overview. (n.d.). Retrieved from: https://www.discprofile.com/what-is-disc/overview/
7. Learn how the CliftonStrengths assessment works (n.d.). Retrieved from: https://www.gallup.com/cliftonstrengths/en/253676/how-cliftonstrengths-works.aspx

Chapter 7

1. DePree, M. (1989). Leadership is an art. New York: Doubleday. MLA Citation. DePree, Max. Leadership Is an Art. New York: Doubleday.

Made in USA - North Chelmsford, MA
1175047_9798672787305
10.06.2020 1045